GW00578647

OLD STONE BUILDINGS

OLD STONE BUILDINGS

Buying · Extending · Renovating

J. A. C. Harrison

DAVID & CHARLES
Newton Abbot London North Pomfret (Vt)

This book is dedicated to the memory of Glyn 'Whiskers' Thomas — not an artist but a crafty craftsman with natural stone, who introduced me to the delights and disappointments of both natural stonework and draught Guinness

'Though you have fallen
The stones still stand!'

British Library Cataloguing in Publication Data

Harrison, J. A. C.
Old stone buildings
1. Buildings—Repair and reconstruction
2. Buildings, stone
I. Title
690'.24 TH3411

ISBN 0-7153-8125-3

Typeset by ABM Typographics Limited, Hull
and printed and bound in Great Britain
by Butler & Tanner Limited, Frome and London
for David & Charles (Publishers) Limited
Brunel House Newton Abbot Devon

Published in the United States of America
by David & Charles Inc
North Pomfret Vermont 05053 USA

Contents

Introduction

During the past few years more and more people have become interested and involved in the improvement of old properties, but have found it difficult to obtain the information they need to tackle major projects. This book attempts to fill the gap by providing comprehensive advice on many aspects of purchase, renovation and extension, particularly those that apply to old rural stone buildings. The major emphasis is on stoneworking but many of the basic principles apply to old brick buildings as well, though the problems involved with stonework are rather more complex.

Old Stone Buildings follows on logically from my previous book *The DIY Guide to Natural Stonework* and indeed was written partly as a result of enquiries provoked by that book. However, it is much broader in scope and is not intended to be simply a DIY manual but a useful guide to all who wish to improve an old property, regardless of whether they plan to do the work themselves or employ builders and contractors to do it for them.

Many of the views expressed are personal and my opinions on taste may well differ from those of the reader. The intention, apart from encouraging good workmanship, is to help the home improver make savings in many areas and avoid disappointments. Since the purchase of a home is for most families their major financial commitment, advice is given on how to judge the viability of this investment and suggestions are made for protecting it and increasing its value. There are also chapters which explain how to reduce significantly the costs of any improvement scheme by employing an architect to produce only the plans that are essential for you to go ahead with the work yourself.

For those happier to delegate everything to the professionals, this book offers some insight into the functions of architects, planning authorities and builders, and provides a guide to their jargon and procedures. This is important, because a knowledgeable client is more likely to have his wishes respected than an ignorant one.

A substantial section of the book has been devoted to the step by step construction of an extension to a small stone cottage, emphasising features of design which reduce the amount of disruption to family life while building work progresses. Since energy costs seem destined to spiral ever higher, this particular project also incorporates built-in insulation features which can reduce overall heat loss by 60 to 70 per cent. In comparison, such widely advertised home additions as double glazing generally achieve less than 10 per cent reduction in heat loss and, in my opinion, are rarely worth the outlay.

As labour becomes more expensive, I hope this book will encourage people to improve and add to the value of old properties by giving them the knowledge and confidence to attempt the work themselves, at a fraction of the cost of handing it all over to the professionals.

PART I: BEFORE YOU START

1

First Considerations

General Comments

Many people have rather idyllic conceptions about owning and 'doing up' a little cottage in the country. Such romantic visions are often rudely dispelled when, after much trauma, reality intrudes upon their dreams. Poets have long eulogised the delights and benefits of country life. Perhaps it is time to redress the balance with a rather more pragmatic approach to what these days is a most expensive venture for anybody.

John Woodeforde goes some way towards dispelling the myth that all was bright and beautiful for the country peasant in the past in his excellent — if sobering — book *The Truth About Cottages* (*see* Bibliography). The picture of poverty and squalor he describes need not be the lot of the cottage dweller today, but those contemplating the country life should bear in mind the following general observations.

For a start, the 'gold-rush' days of the speculative purchase of run-down country properties have quite definitely passed. Any ideas of buying cheaply and 'doing-up' a place with the aid of grants, and making a quick-sale profit, should be firmly squashed. Such ventures are best left to the experienced developers and builders, though even they are now finding the proposition far less attractive than it was a decade ago. This book is not written for such professionals but for those who wish to live with what they create.

In a city or town, houses are largely without special identity in their own right, whereas those standing in isolation, or as part of a small village, contribute to the character and identity of the whole district. Over generations their stability has been more important to the community than their changing occupants. So be prepared to accept that, although on paper *you* own the property, in many ways it will also own you.

The move from a large urban home to a smaller country one can rapidly alter values, bringing into focus many features of life so unthinkingly accepted before. Families understandably contemplate long and hard about emigration from the UK, but few people realise that a move from, say, Birmingham to Toronto may involve less of a change in lifestyle than a move from Birmingham to the Yorkshire Dales. Learning to call a lollipop a popsicle and a pavement a sidewalk may be a lot easier and less painful than learning to avoid the low oak beam in the living room!

But in many more ways than this, not a few ex-city dwellers have been bewildered and disappointed to discover that they cannot cope with the frustrations and limitations that cottage life, in particular, involves. Space is at a premium in a small cottage and there may simply be insufficient room for all the furniture and appliances that normally grace a large urban home. The lounge suite is one of the worst offenders in this instance and looks quite out of proportion in a tiny cottage living room — if you can get it in at all. Treasured or not, it will have to be sold — usually for next to nothing — and a much smaller and less comfortable, yet equally expensive, 'cottage suite' purchased. Next on the list of disappointments is usually the fine old double wardrobe which has to be discarded because it cannot be moved upstairs. Then there is the dressing table which tilts sideways on the uneven bedroom floor and the Welsh dresser which will not stand flush against the curved, misshapen stone walls. In this respect the cottage dwellers of the past were at an advantage — they had virtually no furniture anyway. But such a spartan existence does not suit many people these days. We must have our chairs and tables and fitted units. But in the end you could well find that *all* storage units will have to be purpose made and built-in, not only to save space but also to keep them upright. So, even before you settle in, your cottage will force its identity upon your way of life.

All, however, is not gloom and there can be unexpected bonuses. I was delighted to find that a rather expensive carpet that once graced the sitting room of a Victorian town house has provided fitted carpeting for the whole of the ground floor in my own cottage. But on the whole, lack of space is a problem. Cottages were not built to accommodate such niceties as a child's playroom, study, dining room or guest room. And do not expect to be able to store suitcases, boxes and the ill-fated three-piece suite in the attic — there will not be one. Instead, the children will probably have to share a bedroom and the kitchen may have to double up as dining room and study simply because it is the only room with a large table. Perhaps this is one instance when 'small isn't beautiful'. And, as if smallness and sloping walls and floors are not enough, the country cottage has other defences tucked away for the urban invader — and in particular the six-foot husband. Over the generations we have become taller and generally bigger and modern homes have changed to take account of this. An 'olde-worlde' cottage may have charm but its Lilliputian doorways and low, long-beamed ceilings are likely to cause you more headaches than they gave the original occupants many generations ago. When viewing a cottage for the first time bear in mind that what *seems* charming and quaint may become a major persistent irritation which might cost a considerable amount of money to rectify when you finally come to live in the place.

Looking beyond the front door, you will find that living in a rural area means that not only does your garden impinge on your house but so does the whole of the surrounding countryside. Gone are the grey streets and endless dreary pavements. Instead you have a picturesque country lane which becomes a churned, muddy track after every shower. And, unfortunately, you will probably come to miss that convenient hallway where feet could be wiped and muddy wellingtons and raincoats left to steam unnoticed. More likely the door will open straight into the sitting room, where a fascinating collection of dead animals (lovingly brought home by your happy, country-loving cat) will accumulate, together with the twigs, conkers, birds-nests, acorns, leaves and stones treasured by all children left to their own devices in the great rural outdoors. Even your dog, which you thought would adapt well to country life and be able to exercise itself, has to be kept inside because it chases sheep, pheasants or tractors. It may now be too large to wander around the cottage without being trodden on and thus grows fat sleeping in the only comfortable chair near the fire.

For people with growing families a move to the country could prove to be a very unwise venture and would be better postponed until a later date when the children are grown up. Teenage children, particularly, are unlikely to adjust well, partly because of the disruption to their schooling and the loss of hard-won friendships which occurs in any move and partly because amenities in the country are usually few and far between. The leisure activities which once formed a major part of their lives such as clubs, cinemas, sports, libraries, museums and the general hustle and bustle of a busy city, will either be totally denied to them or else will involve considerable time and expense on your part to provide access to them. Since they are likely to have to travel many miles to school using an infrequent public transport system, school friendships are not easily extended into out-of-school time and even after-school activities may be restricted by the need for routine travel arrangements. The compensations that rural life offers will be alien to many children because they have not grown up in just such a rural environment and are ignorant of it. Very often teenage children become bored, unhappy and perform badly at school after a move from urban to rural life simply because they cannot adjust to the change. It is better to move either while your children are very young or wait until they are old enough to leave home and make the choice for themselves.

There can be problems too for those considering retirement in the country. A modern suburban bungalow is often a more realistic proposition, dull and ordinary though it may seem. Quite apart from the disadvantages already mentioned, the shortage of shops and transport, isolation from neighbours, doctor and social services and the increasing expense of rural existence all combine to turn the bliss of retirement into a possible nightmare of worry.

The comments in this section have obviously been designed to clear the rosy-tinted spectacles of many who look forward to the joys of country life without considering the many disadvantages. There is no doubt that people are incurable hoarders and tend to expand to fill all their available space. Most husbands are only too aware that their wives always manage to fill any newly constructed horizontal surface and still complain about the lack of shelf space! The natural trend is to accumulate more and more belongings and move into larger and larger accommodation. Historically our homes have catered for such a progression. The move from a large urban home to a small rural one is against the natural order of things and requires substantial adjustments to be made. It is only in such comparative isolation that one begins to discover the restrictions that are the reality of country life and the deep dependence upon others that is normally taken for granted.

Practical Observations, Types of Construction

If you intend purchasing an old stone property with a view to modernising and extending it, some knowledge of the basic types of construction is useful from the outset. There are two main categories — mass construction and frame construction — and subsequent alterations will be greatly influenced by the type of construction employed.

Mass Construction

In buildings of this class the walls support the roof load on the foundations as well as providing a weatherproof envelope for the dwelling. Very strong permanent materials such as brick or stone (or both) are used to build the supporting walls which, unlike modern buildings, are

Plate 1 An old Yorkshire Dales farmhouse *G. M. Davies*

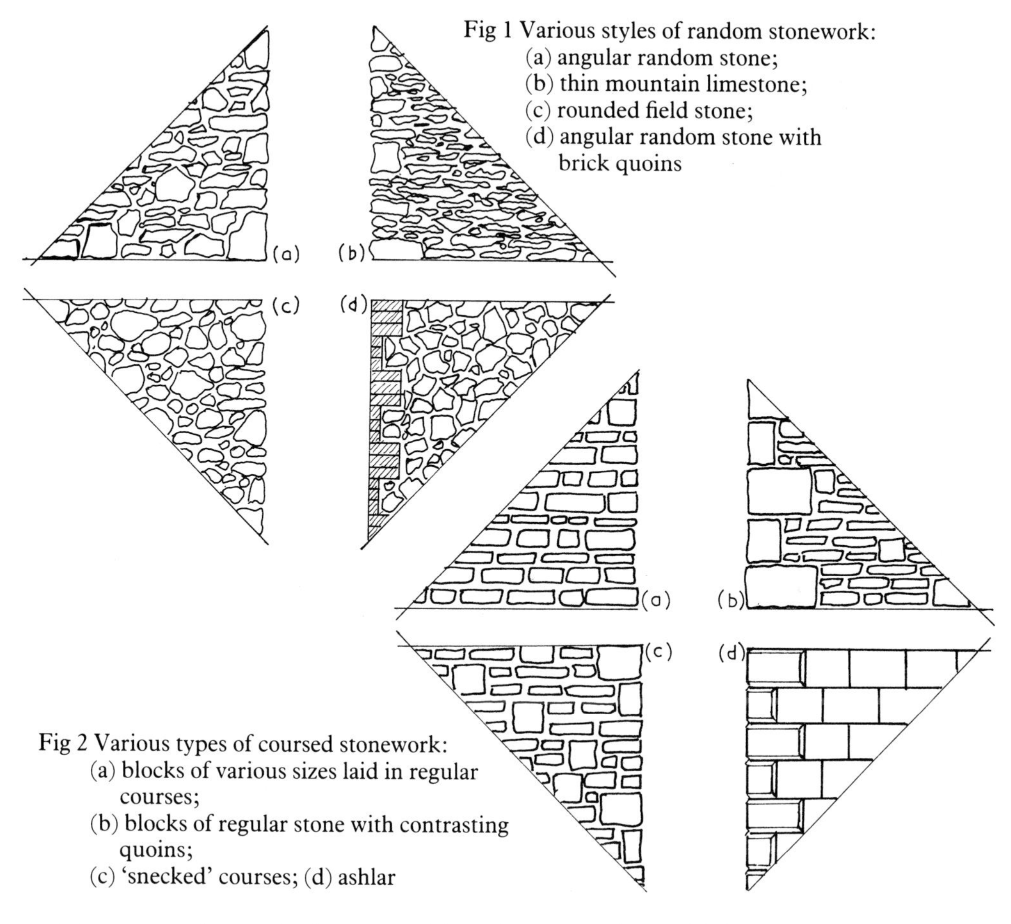

Fig 1 Various styles of random stonework:
(a) angular random stone;
(b) thin mountain limestone;
(c) rounded field stone;
(d) angular random stone with brick quoins

Fig 2 Various types of coursed stonework:
(a) blocks of various sizes laid in regular courses;
(b) blocks of regular stone with contrasting quoins;
(c) 'snecked' courses; (d) ashlar

without a cavity and of substantial and non-uniform thickness. In extreme cases the walls may themselves account for a quarter of the overall ground floor dimensions of the original building.

Dwellings built on mass construction principles may generally be altered and extended without too many problems. The oldest building material is stone and older dwellings will be entirely constructed of stone obtained from the locality. However, not only does the type of stone vary from area to area — the soft limestones characteristic of the Cotswolds being obviously very different from the hard slates of the Lake District — but it can also vary within a fairly small locality, such as the Yorkshire Dales, where irregular mountain limestone occurs together with the readily quarried millstone grit blocks.

The stonework itself may be 'natural', where the individual stones are randomly shaped just as nature produced them and therefore appear in the walls in a wide variety of shapes and sizes without the regular courses seen in brick or blockwork (Fig 1). In better quality building the stone was cut and dressed to make uniform blocks which provided a more regular finish (Fig 2). Very highly worked stone is termed *ashlar* but since it was time consuming and expensive to produce, it was gener-

Plate 2 Large stone house with unusual brick chimney stack and a clay pantile roof.

Plate 3 A barn conversion showing an interesting blend of brick and cobble facework

ally used only for important buildings or corner work, other parts being built using random materials. Between the faces the walls were generally packed with rubble (stone unsuitable for building) and earth. Long ago everything was bonded together with clay but later, as lime became more generally available, lime mortar came into use. The presence of cement in 'old stonework' is clear evidence of a very recent alteration.

In rural areas brick was difficult to obtain, expensive and indeed frowned upon by some stone masons as an inferior material (it still is of course!). It nevertheless became increasingly common as ashlar work declined and is often found where a regular building block was required such as for quoin work at the corners of buildings, or where a heat resistant material was needed for fireplaces and chimney flues (Plate 2 and Fig 3). A mixture of brick and irregular stone can be extremely attractive where patterned work is produced (Plate 3), as seen in the flint/cobble and brick cottages of southern England. However, it can also be most unattractive when used with random stonework and its presence is usually disguised by an outer render. These renders were originally a lime/sand wash which also helped to waterproof the buildings. The later addition of other materials, such as gravel, produced the pebble-dash and stucco finishes which remain today and may totally obscure the true nature of the building material beneath (Fig 3b). Buildings constructed solely of brick are rarely rendered.

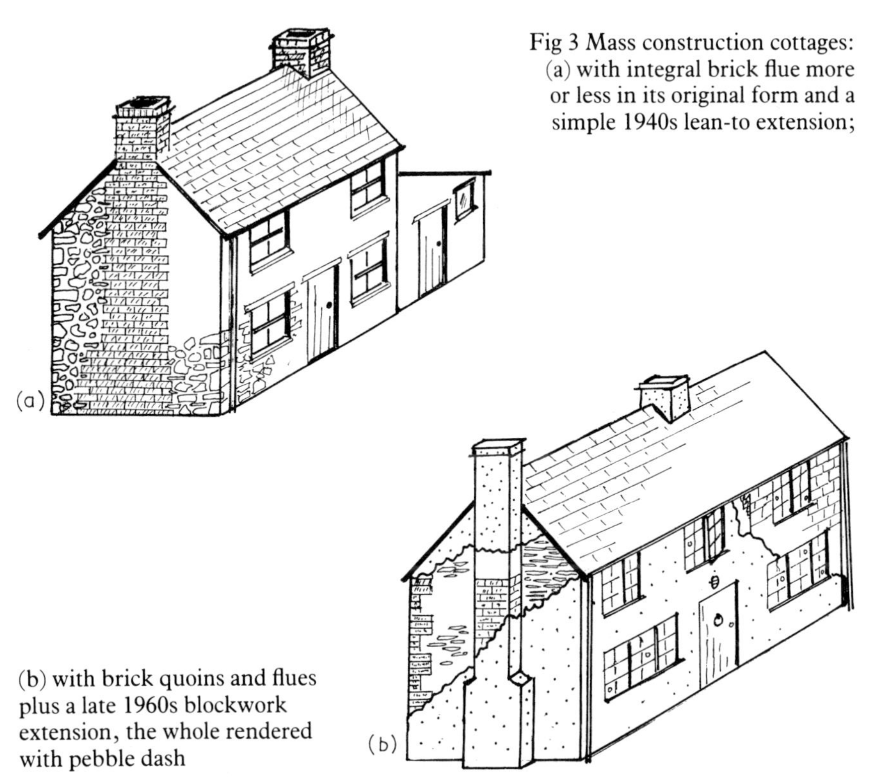

Fig 3 Mass construction cottages: (a) with integral brick flue more or less in its original form and a simple 1940s lean-to extension;

(b) with brick quoins and flues plus a late 1960s blockwork extension, the whole rendered with pebble dash

Plate 4 Typical box-frame construction

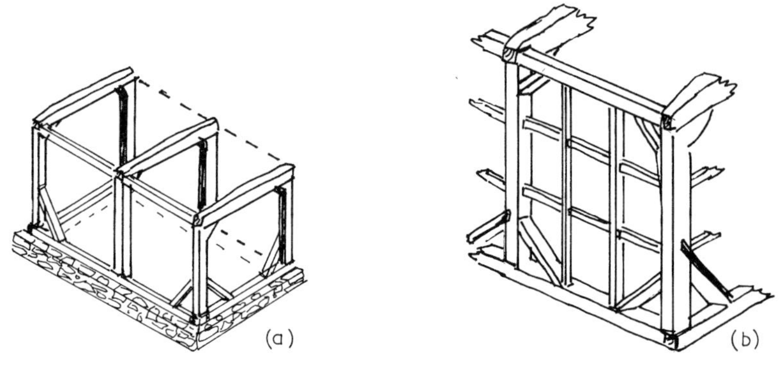

Fig 4 Box-frame construction: (a) outline of the box-frame; (b) detail of additional timber work encountered within one bay

Frame Construction

In such buildings the loads imposed by the roof and floors are carried not by the walls but by a framework which transfers the load to the foundations. The weatherproof skin (ie the walls) is not load-bearing but basically just fills in the spaces between the frame supports. The natural material for frame construction was invariably timber, as in the original Tudor type of house, unlike modern commercial and industrial buildings where iron and steel form the frames.

There are two types of old frame construction based upon different

Plate 5 Small cruck-frame construction farmhouse with stone flags used as the roofing material

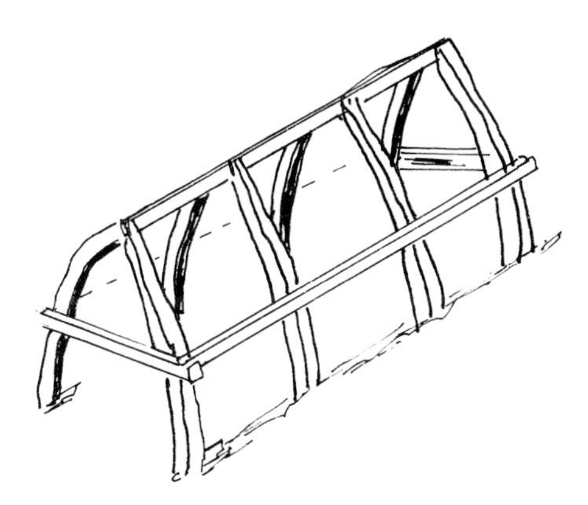

Fig 5 Cruck-frame construction

schools of carpentry. In the Midlands and Southern England the box-frame type of construction, where the roof is carried separately upon a regular framework of vertical and horizontal supports, predominates (Fig 4). The panels between the framework are generally of light materials, originally wattle and daub but later of lath and plaster protected by tiles or weatherboarding. Occasionally the panels are infilled with brick. The structural framework may be either exposed or entirely concealed. Good examples of box-frame construction using such impermanent materials are likely to be old and of historic interest (Plate 4).

The other major type of frame construction is based upon the cruck beam, a technique favoured more commonly in Wales and the North of England. The major features are the paired cruck beams which pass from the foundations to the ridge of the roof, forming an integral part of both the roof and the walls (Fig 5). The walling materials most commonly used were stone and/or brick as in mass construction although the walls were usually of less massive proportions. Cruck-framed buildings of great age still remain and at first sight may be indistinguishable from those erected on mass construction principles (Plate 5).

It is important to ascertain whether or not your property is of the cruck-frame type before planning alterations. Cruck beams cannot be cut away to allow room enlargement without seriously endangering the stability of the whole building and so they place severe limitations on planned extensions. For those wishing to read more about rural cottage construction I can thoroughly recommend R. W. Brunskill's handbooks (*see* Bibliography) which treat the subject in depth. An understanding of the basic principles of the original construction will help greatly in deciding how much can be safely demolished without the need for radical new supports to the roof and how much must be left. However, there are other less obvious limitations to construction changes.

Many old buildings have one of their walls (often a gable end wall) against a road or very close to it and maybe another wall on a boundary, so restricting possible extension to the two remaining directions. Obviously the extension of a cottage within a terraced row is even more limited and problems with excluding light from neighbours' homes may occur. In both cases the cost of extension is likely to be relatively far higher than where an extension can be freely planned. Additional expense is also involved on steeply sloping sites where considerable excavation (perhaps into rock) may be needed to permit an increase in the overall ground area of the habitation.

If the property has not been modernised bear in mind the cost of getting basic services to it. On this point alone be wary of very isolated properties. Providing water and electricity could cost more than the dwelling itself. Mains drainage need not be a problem since a septic tank can usually be installed, but this should still be taken into account when appraising the asking price for a property.

Unless you happen to be connected with the building profession, it is essential to get an old property thoroughly surveyed by a qualified surveyor and to obtain a full written report. The fees may seem expensive but they are worth it; should the building be basically unsound you will be forewarned, should it be in good order the peace of mind alone is worth paying for. But a good surveyor will do more than simply examine and report on the property if you explain your objectives and discuss your fears. The odd cracks in the walls that have been worrying you may be only superficial and offer no cause for concern, but they might have distracted you from more serious — though less obvious — signs of instability.

The surveyor will indicate where you can take down walls and where you cannot. He will point out which parts of the roof are sound and which need replacing, hence indicating a possible place for the insertion of a new roof for an extension. If you engage a good, thorough surveyor you may find subsequent costs reduced substantially.

The fact that a mortgage company have had the property surveyed and are prepared to make an advance is no guarantee that the building is good value. They are only interested in assessing whether they will be able to get back the money they lend you on the property should you default on the mortgage. Their survey has rather different objectives from yours and, in any case, you will not see a copy of their report.

Try to find out if the property has been on the market or unoccupied for a long time. Old buildings, even though perfectly sound, look, smell and *feel* both dilapidated and neglected if not lived in, and if they overwinter without fires they assume a decayed aspect. Do not be put off by this; as a potential buyer it could be to your advantage and may deter less astute competitors. Old properties were built without damp courses or damp-proof membranes but these days proofing against rising damp is a simple and relatively inexpensive process, although replacing timbers affected by such damp may be more costly. Even old yellowed plaster coated with fungus is likely to be only a transient feature associated with neglect, rather than a permanent horror to be inherited with the house.

A lot of people are attracted by the idea of a 'partly modernised cottage', in the estate agent's jargon. Unfortunately there is no strict definition of 'partly' — it simply means that the dwelling is served by some basic services but not all. This could mean a cold water supply, electricity and an outside toilet, or a more extensive modernisation to include hot and cold water, electricity, inside toilet but no bathroom. It does, however, mean that the dwelling is immediately — if not exactly comfortably — habitable, and this alone may justify the extra initial cost compared to an almost derelict 'bargain'.

If you decide to go for this type of property contrary to most professional advice, I would suggest that you live in it for a while just as it is. This is the best way of discovering exactly how you really want the building to be in both practical and aesthetic terms; you will, as it were, understand and work with the basic structure rather than try to impose something alien upon it which you may come to regret later. Neighbours can often offer a wealth of practical and money-saving advice and information. Perhaps one of them is a joiner or plumber and somebody else knows a first-class mason who lives in the next village. By heeding local advice and living in your new home through all the seasons you may find your pipe dream plans would be better relinquished for more practical alternatives.

The Country Cottage as a Second Home

The last couple of decades have seen a tremendous revival of country cottages through their popularity with urban families as second homes and this has produced both positive and negative benefits in rural communities. Undoubtedly the surge of second home buying has saved thousands of what would now be derelict dwellings throughout Britain, at some time abandoned after the exodus of rural families to towns and industrial areas in search of higher living standards after World War II. This conservation is apparently overlooked by those local groups who despise, ignore and harass the owners or users of such homes or, more ironically still, destroy the very dwellings which their local community once chose to abandon but which they now jealously regard as their exclusive heritage.

Unfortunately, as with many events concerning human populations, the pendulum has begun to swing the other way. Now, very old dwellings are rarely being restored, instead it is the habitable dwellings within rural communities that are being sought as second homes by urban families, who, with their higher incomes and better facility for obtaining high mortgages, have pushed the purchase price of such properties beyond the reach of the desperate rural-based house hunter. Thus, owing to a lack of accommodation, young people in country areas are forced away from their natural heritage to an urban existence. As a result, the rural villages, though no longer becoming derelict, stand largely empty for much of the year like some superior type of holiday camp and consequently services, employment and the good old community spirit continue to decline.

There seems no simple answer to this irony, but an awareness of the problem may do much to alleviate the mounting tension between opposing groups. Owners of second rural homes could do much by considering far more the community of which that home was once an integral part. Rather than just using the place for two weeks every summer then closing it down, they should use it as much as possible throughout the year. Here we could learn from our continental neighbours, particularly the French and Scandinavian city dwellers who leave their flats at every opportunity, be it weekend or holiday, and get away to the country. They become known and can contribute to the community. For this reason it is more sensible to have your second home within reasonable travelling distance of your first home. School holidays take up between a quarter and a third of the year, and much of that time can be spent at your second home with working husbands coming down for weekends. 'Out of season' holidays, particularly if your home is in a tourist area, have special rewards.

If you cannot use a second home fully, an alternative is to let it. This should preferably be on a semi-permanent basis at a reasonable rent to a local family in need of housing, with a contract giving you possession for the holiday period. (This should be done through a solicitor to safeguard both parties.) It is a pity to let the place stand empty for eleven months of the year as a constant aggravation to others less fortunate than yourselves.

To the local folk I suggest that they consider the positive side of second home ownership as well as the negative. Such owners are not necessarily very rich. A second holiday home for people with large families is a long term cost effective investment which at the same time enables them to take a regular holiday that otherwise they would not be able to afford. Furthermore, it is these people who are most likely to keep the services and skills of local tradesmen and craftsmen continuing in the community. Benefits to the community as a whole will come if second home owners are welcomed and encouraged to use their homes to the full, rather than treated as outcasts. Perhaps locals could think in terms of exploiting this new influx, rather than feeling that they themselves are the exploited ones.

Some Hidden Problems Concerning Purchase

It is surprising how few people ever look at the deeds of the property they purchase, even though this can reveal a fascinating history behind some of the older dwellings. There are other good reasons, however, for not leaving everything to a solicitor. Solicitors are mainly concerned with verifying that the vendors have an unchallenged right to sell the property, that what is being sold is in fact defined in the deeds, and that there are no proposed developments which can affect your continuing ownership of the property, ie purchase orders on land. They should also draw your attention to boundary disputes and any rights of way which affect your property. But, if you want any more details, you will have to take the trouble to read the deeds.

For example, you may then discover that your property was 'tied' at one time to a large estate or farm and still carries with it certain rights, such as access to common land or the gathering of fuel from nearby woodland. On the other hand, certain responsibilities may also attach to the ownership, such as the maintenance of defined boundaries in a specified manner. I well remember the dismay of a couple who purchased and restored a long-abandoned and isolated cottage with several acres of rough land only to find, too late, that ownership required that they maintain the many miles of crumbling overgrown dry stone walls in good order. They were even more horrified at my quotation for the restoration work. In the end I worked for two weekends with the husband as a pupil and then left him to complete the project. As it turned out he made a first class job of it and found it a most relaxing and enjoyable pastime — but beware!

Other conditions and limitations can also be attached to the property. These may not seem important initially but could become so in the future. For example, look out for separate ownership of mining rights beneath the property. You may find that these are held by a third party and although mining operations may have long ceased they could recommence at a future date. Furthermore, if mining was extensive in the past the possibility of ground subsidence must be considered. Unless asked, your solicitor may feel it unimportant to detail such items, therefore it is always worth while to look at the deeds yourself and then ask the solicitor to clarify any points that are not understood.

Many people, particularly if looking for a second or holiday home, select properties in isolated areas, happily accepting the lack of some basic amenities as the price to be paid for getting away from the pressures of city life. The very attraction of such seclusion, however, may mean that the whole region is of special interest to other people. Before purchase try to find out who is the major landowner in the area and be particularly wary if it is a large government department. In Britain the Ministry of Defence is perhaps the biggest single landowner in terms of acreage, even though much of its property may be leased. In particular it exercises rights over vast tracts of inhospitable land far from urban areas. At any time it could choose to use the area for exercises of a very different kind.

Picturesque isolated valleys with a clear swift river could also prove a less attractive prospect if the local water authority are required to increase the water supply to the urban areas they serve. The demand for water increases with the growth of industrialisation and urbanisation and the most effective way to increase storage capacity and maintain a constant supply is to create reservoirs by drowning valleys in natural watercourses. Sites are generally selected to cause inconvenience to the least number of people, which means picturesque valleys in remote areas.

If the surrounding countryside in upland areas is owned or leased by the Forestry Commission try to find out what their plans are. Conifers grow at an astonishing rate and within a decade the clear views could be gone and your cottage hemmed in by dark spruce, the calls of the buzzard drowned by the wail of chainsaws.

If you are thinking of purchasing a property which is rural and yet convenient to an urban area, consideration must be given to the future growth of that area. The majority of new houses are built in the suburbs of towns and cities and rarely within the city centres, which are now almost exclusively commercial. Thus the built-up area expands to incorporate what were once separate villages and the truly rural areas shrink. The requirements of the urban areas always take precedence over those of the surrounding rural community and the development of motorway and trunk roads, industrial estates and airports could quickly affect the enjoyment of a rural property and its future re-sale.

But nowhere has the rural environment been more drastically altered within the last couple of decades than in the coastal regions. Up until the early 1960s seaside holidays were largely confined to the great Victorian resorts, such as Brighton or Scarborough, which were linked to the rest of the country by excellent road and rail services. Now that most families have their own cars, the whole coastline has become accessible to virtually everyone and, with better roads and faster cars, day-tripping has become increasingly popular. Also, whereas hotel-based holidays were the rule before the car took over, they are now the exception, with most holiday-makers not only cluttering up the coast with their cars but with their personal accommodation in the form of caravans and tents as well.

Many people who twenty years ago purchased property, often very cheaply, in a secluded coastal region to enjoy life in what was then secure tranquillity have had rather a rude shock. 'Beauty spots' are now annually swamped with hordes of cars, caravans and merry campers. Small farms which once cropped corn and potatoes now reap a greater profit from car parks, and caravan and camping sites. The village pub now sports a restaurant, 'surf' bar or smugglers' retreat, sells only pre-packed pies and pasties with canned beer and music, is too crowded in the summer for the locals to get a drink and closes when the season is over. The village shop and Post Office becomes 'Ye Olde Crafte Shoppe' crowded with gas canisters, beach balls and racks of postcards. The local inhabitants have to travel to the nearest town to do their basic shopping along roads made almost impassable by carelessly parked cars.

Areas of many square miles have been irretrievably altered and places like the Gower and Lleyn Peninsulas of South and North Wales now resemble vast holiday camps, solely catering for the short summer invasion of visitors. Unfortunately for the locals, although neglected and deserted, the caravans and car parks remain as eyesores throughout the rest of the year. The only consolation for those who owned or purchased homes originally in such areas is that these properties have become extremely 'desirable' — goodness knows why — and can be sold at a handsome profit enabling a move to an area as yet relatively undiscovered.

2

Finance and Contractors

This is not so much a chapter on how to raise the capital for purchase or alteration to an old property but rather a discussion of where the money is likely to go and how to make the most of it.

Unfortunately, with an erratic rate of inflation, estimation of true amounts (so important to most of us) is out of the question since these would be wildly inaccurate long before this book came into print. Instead, in the Appendix, Table 1, I have attempted to introduce a ratio of costing whereby the overall cost of a project is related to the cost at the time of a basic building item — the theory being that as the cost of this item varies so too will project costs in roughly the same proportion. This should also help to overcome variations in prices around the country owing to transport and other hidden expenses.

When undertaking major changes to a property consideration must be given not only to making a home as you want it but also to protecting and increasing the resale value of a major investment.

Unusual designs, however attractive, ornate and luxury fittings, and expensively landscaped gardens count for far less in resale terms than the basic number and size of rooms. To regain the money spent on such things the price of the property often has to be put well beyond the means of the larger part of the market. The unusual also deters many others whose tastes may be more conservative than your own and your property could well linger on the market for a considerable time or have to be sold for rather less than you spent on it.

Building costs, whether for extensions, renovation, modernisation or simply upgrading and decorating, can be broken down into four groups: materials, labour, professional charges and hidden expenses. Of these only the cost of materials is a basic expense which cannot be avoided by the most determined 'do-it-yourselfer'. But even so, wise buying and shopping around can achieve considerable savings in overall material costs. The highest single item will be labour costs and here the greatest savings can be made depending on how much of the work you are prepared to do yourself. Professional fees for architects or quantity surveyors, vary markedly in proportion to how much assistance is required and can be eliminated completely if you are prepared to sacrifice your time. The hidden expenses occur when unexpected problems arise. Builders generally add a certain amount to their estimate for the job to cover such 'contingencies'.

Building Costs

Having the Work Done for You
The simplest but most expensive way to renovate an old property is to pass the problem over to an architect and a professional builder and leave them to get on with it. It is unlikely that the costs incurred will be recovered on resale of the property except in the long term.

The normal procedure after agreement of the plans with the architect (*see* Chapter 3) is to put the work out to tender. The great temptation is to take the cheapest tender or otherwise settle for the biggest local builder, neither action necessarily being the best. The selection of a builder is of prime importance and if left to the architect it is essential that he has both local knowledge and a thorough briefing.

Modern building techniques are tailored to the erection of new homes on new building sites and to a certain extent are cost controlled. The use of standard plans and standardised pre-formed sections makes building new houses comparatively quicker and cheaper, and hence more profitable, for large builders than coping with the individual problems associated with an old rural stone building. Furthermore, major building firms basically concerned with new developments are unlikely to have employees who are familiar with 'traditional' building practice or used to making major decisions in the face of an unexpected problem.

During a building boom most large firms will either be unwilling to undertake renovation work or else they will make excessive charges to maintain a high level of profitability. The small craftsman/builder is likely to give better value for money in these situations.

During periods of recession, when work in the building trade is scarce, the motto 'any work is better than none' comes into force. Larger firms with their greater capital backing and stockpiled materials can afford to place ridiculously low tenders for work that at other times they would spurn, with the sole aim of ticking over. It is then much harder for the small builder to compete. But it is important to remind yourself that the attractively low tender put in by a large building firm may have hidden catches. The work force will be accustomed to modern buildings, the materials will be those stockpiled for such constructions and you are likely to be pressured into making certain changes to the original specification to accommodate them — or because you are told that something is impossible, whereas in reality it merely requires more skill and effort. Be wary of low tenders at any time but be particularly wary of bargain prices offered by large firms during hard times. Not only is the work likely to disappoint you but there will be less chance to discuss and influence what is being done. Remember too, every specialist small builder who is pushed out of business means less skill and less choice within the industry in the future.

It is better, when choosing a builder to carry out work on an old property, to consider the total suitability of that builder for the job.

Seek out firms who regularly undertake such work, particularly those that have worked in the area. Go and look at other jobs that they have undertaken and judge for yourself if their style will suit you. Find the answers to a few important questions: were their previous customers satisfied? Is the interior finish as good as the outside would indicate? Was the manager available when required? Did he work on site with his men? Do they specialise in the particular types of work you want undertaken?

When you have found a builder who seems to satisfy all requirements it is worth spending some time discussing your plans with him. His skill and experience could save you considerable expense since he will be far more familiar with the problems of taking old buildings apart than the architect, who is basically concerned only with adding new pieces to them. The builder may be able to suggest several practical alterations to your plans to simplify the work. For example, perhaps a certain opening would be better sited a foot away from where you planned it. Conversely, he might be more willing to tackle a difficult problem than you anticipated.

In such a situation costs are always negotiable and you may be able to reach a price for the job which satisfies all parties. If you are going to live in the house while the work is being carried out then from the outset you will be able to discuss a procedure which allows you some degree of comfort and the builder some flexibility. An additional percentage will almost certainly have to be paid to compensate the builder for the additional inconvenience of having to keep the place clean and secure at all times and ensure an uninterrupted supply of basic services. If you are paying not to be inconvenienced then insist that you are not. An acquaintance made do with a bucket for eleven weeks after his 'builders' had thoughtlessly demolished a partition wall on to the lavatory.

Having agreed total price and procedure, tricky problems, such as negotiating stage payments and penalty clauses, remain. If you are employing an architect you can pass these matters over to him; but on the whole architects (*see* Chapter 3) adhere rather too rigidly to modern building practice where certain stages in the growth of a house can be easily identified and two or three substantial payments made at these stages. With renovation and extension work, however, particularly where a small builder is involved, a larger number of smaller payments is preferable. This offers protection for both the client, who is paying for work done, and the builder, who needs a regular income. Otherwise the builder is often forced to raise money for materials to enable him to get on with the work. He may well pass on the interest he has to pay on such loans in additional charges to you.

Generally speaking the builder/client relationship begins well but tends to deteriorate — mainly perhaps because of general impatience all round to see the job finished. This is especially true if bad weather or some unexpected hitch holds up the work for long. Building work usually progresses faster in the summer than in the winter because of better weather and longer daylight hours.

At the start of the job the work appears to progress at a phenomenal rate, walls rise, roof timbers sprout and are covered within a matter of a week or two and the client feels that the job is coming to an end. In fact the work is far from complete. It is vital that the builder get the roof on as soon as possible to provide weather protection for all the interior work and, understandably, much of the inessential work is left to a later stage. Completion of the job after the shell is erected may well take twice as long as getting the shell up and days may pass with very little change apparent. It is also at this stage that clients tend to start altering the plans, making changes and additions which may seem minor but disrupt the builder's continuity of work.

As a final note — beware of 'cowboy' builders. These are generally unskilled jobbers who quote very low prices, do poor quality work and often leave before completing it in favour of a more lucrative job elsewhere. Avoid employing anyone who cannot command a good reference.

Getting Involved Yourself

As pointed out earlier, in renovation work labour is by far the most expensive commodity, so the more of your time you devote to assisting with the job the less you will have to pay for someone else's time. There are various ways in which you can be involved and these will depend upon the amount of time you have available, your age, general health and the degree of confidence you feel in tackling some of the more skilled aspects of building.

Much of the architect's work can be taken over by the clients, especially if they are already living in the property. In fact, with the builder's help, you may be able to dispense with the architect altogether and draw up and submit your own plans. A good compromise if you have had no previous experience is to engage an architect to produce a scale plan of the existing property for a fixed fee (a survey plan), and use copies of the plan to produce the new design, employing the same symbols and layout as the architect.

If you are fit and enjoy physical effort, then instead of jogging or going to the squash club, try labouring for the builder on your own home. It will save money and give immense satisfaction. There will be a lot of demolition work and preparation, requiring little or no skill, before the builder can make a start. Gateways will have to be widened to cope with bulk delivery of materials, and a hard standing area for those materials and for mixing cement will have to be prepared. All soil and vegetation must be cleared away from the whole area where a new extension is to be built. None of these jobs requires much skill but they take time and effort. Do remember, however, to save and clean the old materials for future re-use. This is particularly important if you are knocking down old outbuildings or garden walls since the stone and timbers are likely to match those of the house itself. Demolition is discussed in more detail in Part III.

I do not recommend you start demolishing internal walls or window openings without the builder being present, unless you are undertaking full responsibility for the building and doing it largely yourself (*see* Part II). As the building progresses, you might like to labour for the builder by mixing cement, carrying materials and generally lending a hand. If you are in regular employment a certain amount of thought must be put into the timing. For example, concrete the foundations over a weekend if the builder is agreeable, take your fortnight's leave while the walls are being built and, most important, start the job in the spring so that you have the advantages of long daylight hours and generally better weather when the outside work is being done. By autumn, when the nights are drawing in again, you should be finishing off indoors. It is at this later stage that the greatest savings can be made. Glaze your own windows: you will be surprised how quick you become after the first two or three panes. Do all your own painting, staining and sanding. Do not employ the builder to put up shelves and cupboards, do it yourself.

But, be warned, one of the few jobs which is best left to the professionals is plastering.

Taking Over from the Builder

With a little confidence, a lot of background reading and perhaps a bit of practice on a garden wall or an outbuilding, you might feel able to do away altogether with the builder as a main contractor. This is not such a drastic step as at first it sounds. Builders these days often employ various sub-contractors to carry out certain parts of the work: for example, bricklayers or masons to put up the shell, plumbers for water and heating services, electricians for the wiring, joiners for timber work and roofing contractors for tiling or slating. These sub-contractors give a fixed price for the job, including or excluding materials; the main contractor adds on a percentage for his efforts as coordinator and passes the cost on to the client. By directly employing sub-contractors to carry out those portions of the work which you do not feel able to tackle, you can do away with the builder's profit and save considerable expense.

Generally, sub-contractors prefer to have the materials ready for them on site and usually they will state their requirements when they price the job. It is essential to obtain a fixed price contract from them before they start and that both parties adhere to it. Do not accept estimations — these are generally set too low to secure a contract and the final price is much higher.

By providing the materials you avoid delays in starting or breaks in the continuity of the work. When sub-contractors order materials, it is often easier for them to be overgenerous with their calculations and for any excess to be considered a 'perk'. You should make it clear that surplus materials must not be removed. Tools can often be misplaced or taken inadvertently so keep your own tools stored safely away to avoid confusion.

The non-professional, however, is at a disadvantage when purchasing materials, compared with a registered builder. Building materials are subject to VAT and, unlike the builder who is VAT registered, the ordinary person cannot claim the tax back. In theory, therefore, builders should obtain materials more cheaply and be able to pass this saving on to the client, since building work itself is zero-rated. In practice this does not often happen and so any disadvantage for the person acting as his own main contractor may be only theoretical.

Great savings, however, may be made by careful timing of the purchase of materials and this should go ahead well before the building work starts. Inflation will always push up the cost of materials at a higher rate than your capital can earn interest. So buy up all the non-perishable materials you are going to need at the start and store them well. This also avoids delays at a later date owing to unavailability of goods through transport difficulties, market shortages and strikes. Buy in bulk and negotiate a cash discount — builders' merchants much prefer cash to accounts and should be willing to reflect this in their pricing. But do not buy perishable commodities such as cement and plaster in vast quantities, and store what you do buy in a clean, dry, covered area. Cement quickly deteriorates, especially in a dampish atmosphere. Cover sand to keep it dry and prevent it being washed away in a downpour, blown away in a gale or trampled around by the local kids. Also, have it tipped on a clean, hard, working area beside the mixer to avoid the mess and wastage involved in moving it around later.

For somebody without building experience the calculation of the quantities of materials required is an extremely difficult and daunting task. Therefore even for the determined 'do-it-yourselfer' I recommend engaging the services of a quantity surveyor. Provide him with a copy of the plans and the specification (*see* Chapter 3) and he will draw up a complete list of the materials you require and the quantities needed — this is termed a bill of quantities. This will avoid any miscalculation of the overall cost through over or under ordering of the major building materials and the omission of small items such as nails, wall ties and paint.

Doing It All Yourself

Draw up an outline plan of action right from the beginning. Do not rush blindly into the work without a thought of where logically to continue with a subsequent stage. Approach the work professionally and not as a hobby. Remember that you are likely to take at least twice as long to do the same job as an experienced builder, so a large extension must be viewed as a long term project. I would certainly encourage the employment of sub-contractors by anyone considering doing most of the work themselves, particularly where some expertise is required, for example in plastering, or where many tools of a rather specialist nature are needed, for example for the basic electrical wiring and plumbing.

When tackling the work themselves many people forget the hidden cost of essential tools. These days even basic tools are expensive and whether purchased or hired they should be chosen wisely and looked after. In *The DIY Guide to Natural Stonework* I have devoted a chapter to discussing the basic tools needed for building the shell of a house and how to care for them. Some general information about tools and equipment can also be found in Part II of this book.

Do not run away with the idea that by doing it yourself the job is going to be cheap — it is not — but it should be considerably less expensive than having it all done for you. Always remember that the property, as well as being a home to be proud of, is an investment which may one day have to be realised. Make a good job of what you do and take the work down and start over again if you are not satisfied with it.

Grants

Council grants are available for the renovation and improvement of old properties and for unlisted properties (those of no particular historical or architectural interest). All are the responsibility of the district councils, whereas listed properties are generally the responsibility of the county councils. In the majority of councils all matters concerning grants come under the Department of Environmental Health and not Planning, Architects or Building Departments as one might imagine. A booklet entitled *Your Guide to House Renovation Grants* can be obtained from the council and anybody wishing to apply for a grant is strongly urged to get the guide and follow its advice.

Within the context of this book only two types of grant need be considered:

1 *Improvement grants* for improving existing dwellings to a high standard.
2 *Intermediate grants* for providing certain standard amenities which are missing.

Regardless of the type of grant, certain features and standards apply.

The amount of the grant is based upon what is termed the 'eligible expense' which is a sum determined by the council for carrying out the work required to a certain standard. The grant is a percentage of this eligible expense, generally 60 per cent in improvement areas and 50 per cent elsewhere. If the limit of the eligible expense is set at £5,000 for an improvement grant, the amount payable will be £3,000 in an improvement area or £2,500 otherwise, and not the full £5,000 as some people mistakenly believe.

The grants are provided for the improvement of sound pre-1961 properties and the applicant must either be a freeholder or have a lease with at least five years to run. Grants are not normally available for the improvement of properties to be used as second homes and the applicant will have to sign a certificate declaring that for a period of five years the property will be his sole or main residence. However, if the property is intended to be let then the applicant must declare himself a landlord and certify that the property will be let as a residence for five years and not as holiday accommodation. No holiday homes can now be renovated with the aid of council grants. If these conditions are breached then the council may demand part or complete repayment of the grant together with interest. So it is important to check whether a property you are interested in purchasing for a holiday home has received a grant within the past five years. If so, you might find yourself having to pay part of it back.

Applications for grants must be made on the standard forms provided by the council and no work should be started until grant approval has been obtained. (This is not the same as planning approval.) Furthermore, a time limit for completion of the work may be imposed — do-it-yourselfers in particular should be aware of this — but it will not be less than one year. Similarly, the council will need to be satisfied that the work is to be carried out to a certain standard of workmanship; and since payment is not made until the work is completed and inspected the grant can be withheld if that standard is not met. With large grants an instalment payment may be made at the discretion of the council, for example 50 per cent of the total grant when 75 per cent of the work is finished.

Improvement Grants

Improvement grants are available to help owners improve older houses to a good standard, not to assist with improvements to properties already fully equipped and in good repair, nor to provide more space by the addition of further rooms. When considering whether an applicant is eligible for a grant, the council are concerned with what the property will be like on completion and not what it lacks at present; improvement grants cannot be used for itemised additions without regard for the total condition of the property. To this end councils require that the property on completion will have a useful life of at least thirty years and will conform to what is termed *the ten-point standard,* which is condensed in the chart in Fig 6.

If three or more of the items listed in the ten-point standard are absent or sub-standard in the dwelling then normally an application for an improvement grant will be successful. But it must always be borne in mind that on completion the ten-point standard has to be satisfied. People who cannot afford to carry out all the work in this standard and choose perhaps to make only partial improvements, with the object of doing further work at a later stage, should make an application for an in-

The dwelling upon completion must:

1. be free from damp
2. have adequate light and ventilation for each room
3. have adequate and safe provision for artificial lighting and electrical socket outlets
4. have adequate drainage facilities
5. be structurally sound
6. have satisfactory internal arrangement
7. have adequate facilities for preparing and cooking food
8. have adequate facilities for heating
9. have proper means for storing fuel and refuse
10. conform with the regulations in force concerning the thermal insulation of the roof

Fig 6 Outline of the ten-point standard for home improvement grants

termediate grant instead. It is important to bear in mind that the improvement grant commits the applicant to considerable expenditure on his own part since certain features which may not have been regarded as essential will have to be included. The idea that 'if I do the work myself the grant will cover the cost' is totally wrong.

The fact that the property has in the past received a grant for improvement does not necessarily preclude a new application form being successful, although adjustments may be made to take into account the earlier grant. Similarly, buildings previously not used as homes (domiciliary dwellings in the jargon), such as old farm buildings, may, at the discretion of the council, be eligible for a grant for conversion to homes. In such situations the appropriate council officers must be consulted before an application is made.

Intermediate Grants

Intermediate grants are available for improving housing by providing missing standard amenities such as bath, sink, water closet, and so on. As with improvement grants, certain standards must be satisfied. These are outlined in Fig 7 and are less comprehensive than the ten-point standard. To satisfy the requirement for roof insulation in all cases a separate home insulation grant should be applied for in addition to the intermediate grant application.

Intermediate grants are ideal for the improvement of the partially modernised home — perhaps replacing an external water closet with an internal one — or where the DIY person wishes to carry out improvements in a number of discrete stages over a period of time without undertaking major structural alterations to the property. However, if the addition of a standard amenity involves extra work, such as the installation of a septic tank in connection with the water closet, or an extension to accommodate a bathroom, it would probably be better to apply for an improvement grant instead.

When an application for a grant is considered it is important to consult the council officers concerned. They are not faceless bureaucrats demanding completion of endless forms. On the contrary they can explain the situation in a matter of moments and advise on the best and correct approach in your particular circumstances. Furthermore, where costs occur above the original estimated eligible expense that could not have been foreseen earlier, adjustments can be made at the discretion of such officers.

To qualify for the grant the following conditions need to be fulfilled:

1 Basic requirements applicable to all grants
2 Amenities are for the sole use of the occupants
3 The dwelling must be in a good state of repair
4 The dwelling must satisfy the thermal insulation requirements for roof spaces
5 In all other respects the dwelling must be fit for habitation
6 The building must be likely to be available for use as a dwelling for at least 15 years

Fig 7 Outline of the six-point standard for intermediate grants

Mortgages

In the UK finance for house purchase is provided mainly by building societies who at present supply between 85 per cent and 95 per cent of all home loans. The majority are on modern properties with only about 20 per cent of the total lent being on older dwellings, that is houses built before 1919. However, since such buildings (about 6 million in total) form no more than 30 per cent of the total housing stock, this discrepancy is not as large as it would at first appear.

When considering a mortgage application building societies seem to adhere to three main criteria and should any one of these not be satisfied the application is almost certain to be unsuccessful. Firstly, the property is the security against which the loan is made. The building society must be satisfied that it can be readily sold to realise a sum which would both repay the oustanding loan and cover any costs incurred. The building society's survey of the property is solely to estimate this resale value, which may be considerably lower than the purchase price.

Secondly, the applicant must satisfy the building society that he or she is able to repay the loan by regular instalments over the period agreed. The amount of the loan will be influenced by the salary and nature of employment of the applicant. In recent years average house prices have increased in line with average earnings, remaining about three and a half times average annual income. This means building societies are able to fix the maximum loan in relation to the earnings of the applicant. At present this figure is about two and half times annual gross income, with a further adjustment for a spouse who is also employed. Obviously the age of the applicant will also be taken into consideration.

The third criterion is more difficult to define and has nothing to do with the financial eligibility of the applicant. Building societies are under a moral obligation to provide finance primarily for those in particular need of a home, for instance first time buyers and those moving from one house to another. They will not normally finance the purchase of holiday cottages or second homes.

It is with older properties in isolated areas that the first criterion is generally the most difficult to satisfy, since they have become somewhat overpriced. Would-be rural cottage buyers should not be surprised to find the maximum mortgage allowable as low as 50 per cent of the purchase price, even if they satisfy all the other conditions. In addition, large building societies in general do not allow mortgages on properties which are not modernised, nor will they finance modernisation.

In fact this can be something of a 'Catch-22' for the cottage buyer. If the property is to be modernised, the building societies will provide a mortgage once the work has been completed but the work will have to be financed by alternative means, such as a bank loan. This is fine for those who already have a mortgage and can take out a second mortgage on the improved property, or simply increase the mortgage on the original dwelling which will have increased in value over the years. On the other hand, those who purchase an old cottage from savings, raise a loan to modernise the property, and then apply for a mortgage to pay off that loan and to take advantage of tax benefits, may find their application unsuccessful. This is because the third criterion is no longer satisfied — the applicant has a home and is not in need of housing, so the mortgage is technically for the purpose of repaying another loan, not for purchasing property. This problem of course applies only to first-time buyers. Those moving from a property with an existing mortgage can carry this mortgage facility over to their next home and finance any improvements on their new one by using the profit from the sale, or by obtaining a second mortgage.

Whereas the above criteria are adhered to fairly rigidly by the major building societies, numerous smaller societies exist to cater for 'special cases' and since they are prepared to take a greater risk, they charge slightly higher rates of interest. It is to such organisations that people wishing to purchase a somewhat run-down rural cottage should turn if they need finance and are unsuccessful with the major societies. In rural areas many of these smaller societies specialise in providing just such a service and estate agents can be very helpful in directing a would-be purchaser to an appropriate source of finance.

For all first-time buyers, and those moving home after several years, it is best to adopt a 'back to front' approach to buying a property. Do not set out to find your dream home and set your heart on a property only to have your mortgage application turned down. Go to the building society of your choice first, explain the type of property you are seeking and be directed by them. You will be told what they are prepared to lend and on what sort of dwelling. Go house hunting from the start in that price range to avoid disappointment later. Furthermore, they will advise on the best type of mortgage to suit your particular requirements and explain additional government assisted home loan schemes for first-time buyers.

In addition to registered building societies, local councils also provide mortgage facilities. However, since the availability of such loans and the criteria applied vary widely throughout the UK, it is best to make a direct approach to the council early in your search for a property.

Home owners wishing to improve their properties might be tempted by advertisements from finance companies in the press. Anybody contemplating such a loan is strongly advised to consider the amount of interest being charged — often as high as 30 per cent per annum (and without any tax benefit). If one can afford to make such payments then the money needed could be saved over a couple of years in a building society and the improvements paid for outright instead of being paid for several times over during a specified loan period. More important still, improvements financed in this way are never likely to increase the value of the property sufficiently to recoup the total sum paid out.

3

Planning, Architects and Plans

Anybody contemplating building a new home, extending an existing dwelling or converting some other type of building should consult the local planning authority, and probably an architect, before the plans for it can be drawn up and submitted correctly. In rural areas with special local identity, or where stone buildings occur in their original form and are of historic interest, it is particularly important to consult the planning authorities before going ahead with any specific ideas for alteration.

Planning

Why Planning?

The need for planning has arisen basically as a direct consequence of advances in communication and transport in recent times. The constraints upon where one has to live have largely disappeared and so have the constraints upon where one obtains the materials to build a home. In addition, people see on television different areas and countries, with different cultures and architecture. The identity of our rural communities, which were originally based upon the local availability of materials and local craftsmen trained to use them, can easily be disrupted by the importation of ideas, materials and styles totally alien to the area. The function of local planning is to attempt to retain the historical, functional and visual integrity of an area. It prevents outlandish developments which suit personal egos only and promotes those which blend with the surroundings. It puts a brake upon the proliferation of modern follies. A good example is the couple who wished to commemorate their honeymoon in Majorca by converting a barn in the Yorkshire Dales into a Spanish hacienda. Needless to say their application was turned down.

However, unusual designs suited to the environment which make use of traditional materials and styles may well be viewed not only sympathetically but excitedly by planning authorities. Local planning departments do not work by fixed rules and regulations, but rather within a framework of guidelines which are flexible, allowing modern substitute materials in areas where the traditional ones are no longer freely available, and generally allowing extensions so long as these do not make a mockery of the original building.

To a certain extent planning officers see their role as a negative one. It is far easier to tell the applicant what he may *not* do than to provide an infinite list of what is allowed. It is this very negative approach which leads people to view planning authorities with suspicion and even distaste. It is refreshing to see that some councils are now publishing guidelines for the general public which not only explain planning views, but also describe what is, and what is not, acceptable in planning terms.

Much of their work involves maintaining the 'status quo' of an area. People move for various reasons. There are those for whom work dictates a move and others who suddenly have the freedom to move to an area which offers them special amenities; the sea, mountains, fishing, sailing and so on. As far as planners are concerned this is no excuse for being dissatisfied with the local architecture and wanting to drastically alter a new home. Houses cannot be purpose built to personal requirements without some regard for the harmony of the surrounding district.

Submission of Plans

If submitting plans drawn up by yourself it is foolhardy to prepare these without prior consultation with local planning officers. Whereas planning authorities who reject proposed plans are bound by statute to provide reasons for their rejections, they are under no obligation to suggest acceptable alternatives. It is far better to gather together your ideas, do some rough sketches and make an appointment to discuss these with somebody in the planning department before you attempt to draw up the final plans for submission. It is a free service, after all, and not only might you be told *why* your proposals are likely to be unacceptable but in the course of the discussion you may be given help and guidance as to how your particular plans might be brought in line with local planning requirements. However, do not expect council officials to recommend particular architects or builders. They are not allowed to do this in law and the very suggestion could cause embarrassment.

It is also as well to be aware that the trained planning officers you consult do not in fact make the final decision as to whether or not a particular proposal will be passed and the project given permission to proceed. The final decision is made by a planning committee, which consists entirely of locally elected council members. These are lay people, only advised by the permanent planning officers. Should you disagree with the advice of the planning officers and still feel that your proposals are reasonable, these can be submitted to the planning committee in their original form and still stand a chance of being passed. Furthermore, the decision of the planning committee itself need not be final since facilities for appeal are also available.

The maximum number of copies of the plans which the council can legally request is four and many planning departments require less, so reducing the expense. A copy of the specification is not normally required, although details of the types of materials to be used are sometimes requested.

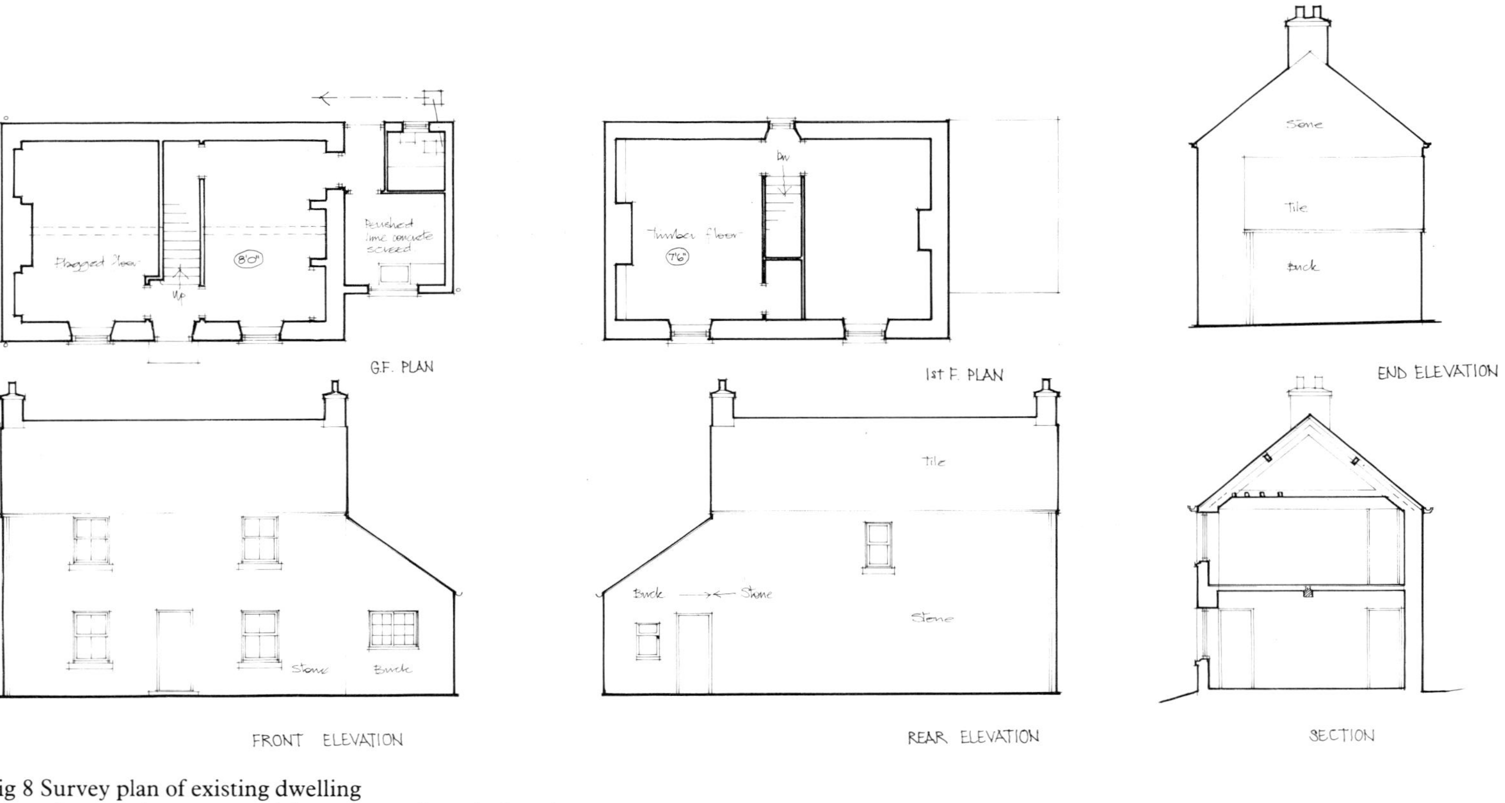

Fig 8 Survey plan of existing dwelling
a Survey plan — ground floor plan and south elevation
b Survey plan — first floor plan and north elevation
c Survey plan — east elevation and section

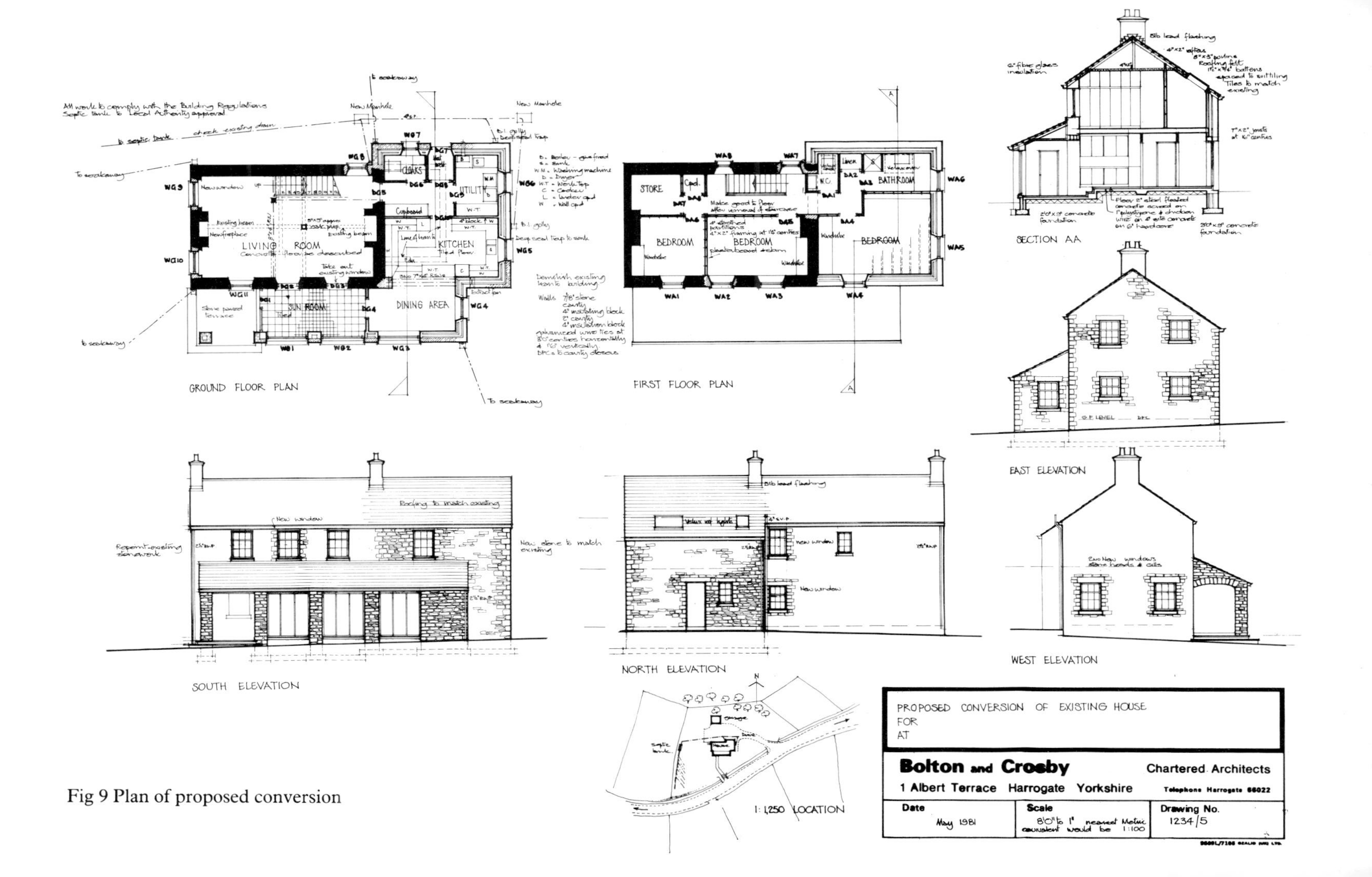

Fig 9 Plan of proposed conversion

Planning Permission

No building work may commence until full planning permission has been obtained, and no alteration to the originally submitted plans may be made without prior consultation with the planning authorities. Minor alterations may be allowed after consultation, without the need to re-submit new plans. Land purchased for building should not be bought 'on spec' but with outline planning permission. This means that a house of suitable character may be built on the land when plans have been submitted and accepted. If purchased with full planning permission then the plans already submitted must be followed unless permission for a different type of dwelling is obtained.

Extensions and Conversions

The main objective of planning is to ensure that any extension to a property is in keeping with the character of the original, both in style and building materials. Huge dormer windows in a small low cottage, or a brick-faced, flat roofed extension on an old stone building will obviously be unacceptable. Less obviously unacceptable, however, are alterations to the roof pitch or the distance between the extension and a neighbouring dwelling. In the case of the latter it is as well to consult your neighbour before drawing up the plans, since it is likely that the planning officers will do so in any case once proposals are submitted and they will certainly take into account any objections expressed.

In general, planning permission is not required for alterations which will not significantly change the external appearance of a building. Conversions such as putting windows into an outbuilding may not need the submission of plans but this should be checked with local planning officers first.

Listed buildings, that is those designated as being of historical or architectural interest, will be examined more critically by planning departments. They will tend to be more sympathetic to development proposals if these are likely to save the building from becoming derelict. In this category come the conversion of buildings such as old stone field barns, toll houses, water mills and country stations, many of which have been saved by skilful conversion into dwellings. The solicitor's search should reveal whether or not the building is listed and, if so, you should make certain that there are no attendant clauses, such as the maintenance of lock gates, for instance. Perhaps the major stumbling block in such conversions, but one that is often overlooked by the hopeful applicant, is the situation of the building. Where it is remote, providing adequate access roads and basic services could so alter the general landscape that planning permission would be refused, however acceptable the proposed alteration to the building itself.

Architects

An architect is basically a designer of buildings but, in addition, is qualified to assist in several other aspects of building. His fees are dependent on how much is required of him and may be calculated either on an hourly basis or as a fixed percentage of the total cost of the work planned.

Used to his full extent the architect will visit and survey the site and draw up a survey plan, which will include any dwelling to be altered or extended. Working with this survey plan (Fig 8) he will design the new building or extension and provide scale plans (Fig 9) for submission to the client, planning department, water authorities, and so on, in, addition to a working plan and specification for the builders. Once planning permission has been granted, the architect will put the work out to tender or select a builder, visit the site regularly to oversee the building work and ensure that various regulations and requirements are being met. If required, he will make stage payments to the builders at the appropriate times on behalf of the client. In effect, the architect takes over the total responsibility for the building from the client and the fees will reflect this.

Few people have either the sufficient knowledge or time to do all the work themselves, so at least some of the services of an architect will be required. I used an architect to prepare the plans shown in Figs 8–11 to demonstrate how such plans should be properly presented. The fees for providing a complete set of drawings are approximately 1 per cent of the total cost of the proposed extension and renovation, but these costs may be substantially reduced if you are prepared to do some of the work yourself.

Generally, people are unsure of what scales to use for the drawings, what symbols are required and which plans and elevations are necessary. I have tried to give all the information required in the plans shown in Figs 8 and 9. The cheapest way to make use of an architect's services would be to engage one to draw up the survey plan of your property as in Fig 8. Using those drawings, plus the information in this book, it is relatively simple to produce plans for an extension which will meet the various requirements. This should certainly halve the architect's fees and involve you in no more than a few days' work. It will also help you to decide where you want various rooms to be situated rather than just accepting the architect's opinions.

The major drawback to this method is that you will be unable to approach the architect should unexpected problems occur at either the planning or building stage, so this is really only for the confident and determined do-it-yourselfer.

Most people engage an architect to draw up and submit the plans and specification for them but then take over the supervisory role of the architect. This will obviously be the case if you are undertaking some of the building work yourself. In this instance it would be perfectly proper to consult the architect from time to time and such consultation is unlikely to incur further expense.

Architect-drawn plans and proposals stand a better chance of meeting building requirements and obtaining planning approval than those produced by a non-professional. This is because architects have all the necessary information to hand, plus long experience of designing buildings to meet both local and national requirements. They avoid errors which, although minor, might mean all the difference between acceptance and rejection. Even apparently small internal structural alterations to room layout may necessitate further modifications, such as the installation of extra windows, to satisfy the regulations for adequate illumination. This could well be overlooked by the inexperienced person whereas it would be an automatic consideration for an architect. Anybody attempting to produce their own plans, therefore, should not only visit the planning department first but should also obtain a copy of the Building Regulations, published by HMSO, and read them well.

Even if you are employing an architect to provide the drawings you should still involve yourself as much as possible with their preparation. Get a copy of the survey plan and use it to generate your own ideas for renovation and extension, which you can then discuss with the architect. At this planning stage it is particularly important to consider domestic routine if the property is to be occupied whilst the building work is carried out. Design any extension to allow normal functioning of the home to continue as long as possible and keep any disruptions to a minimum.

The design adopted in the drawings (Figs 8–11) allows for this by the simple expedient of building the new extension totally around an earlier kitchen extension which will subsequently be demolished. As there are no common walls between the new and old extensions, demolition can be delayed until the new extension is almost completed. Attention to such matters at the planning stage can save considerable upset later.

Plans and Specifications

Examples of architects' drawings, to the standard required for submission to clients and the various authorities, are reproduced in Figs 8 and 9 and are largely self-explanatory. However, to help the uninitiated interpret them, I have annotated one plan view and the section in Figs 10 and 11. Drawings for a proposed extension are in two sets, the survey drawings (Fig 8) and the plans for the new work (Fig 9). These drawings are first made on tracing paper then printed on dye-line copy paper of standard sizes, most commonly A1 which measures 420mm x 594mm (approximately 17in x 24in).

The layout of each of the drawings follows a similar format which must show the ground floor plan (Fig 9a), the first floor plan (Fig 9b),

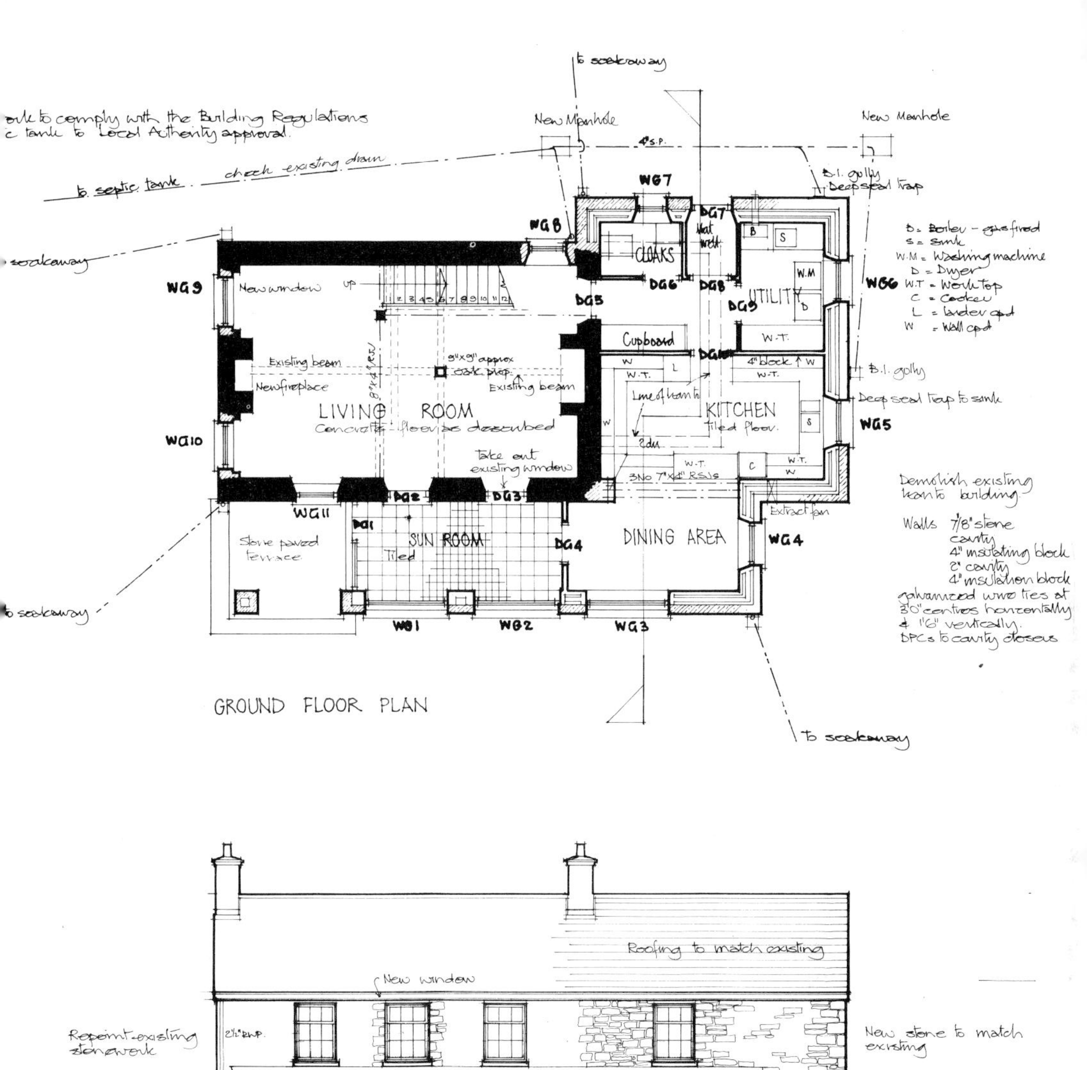

Fig 9a Proposed conversion — ground floor plan and south elevation

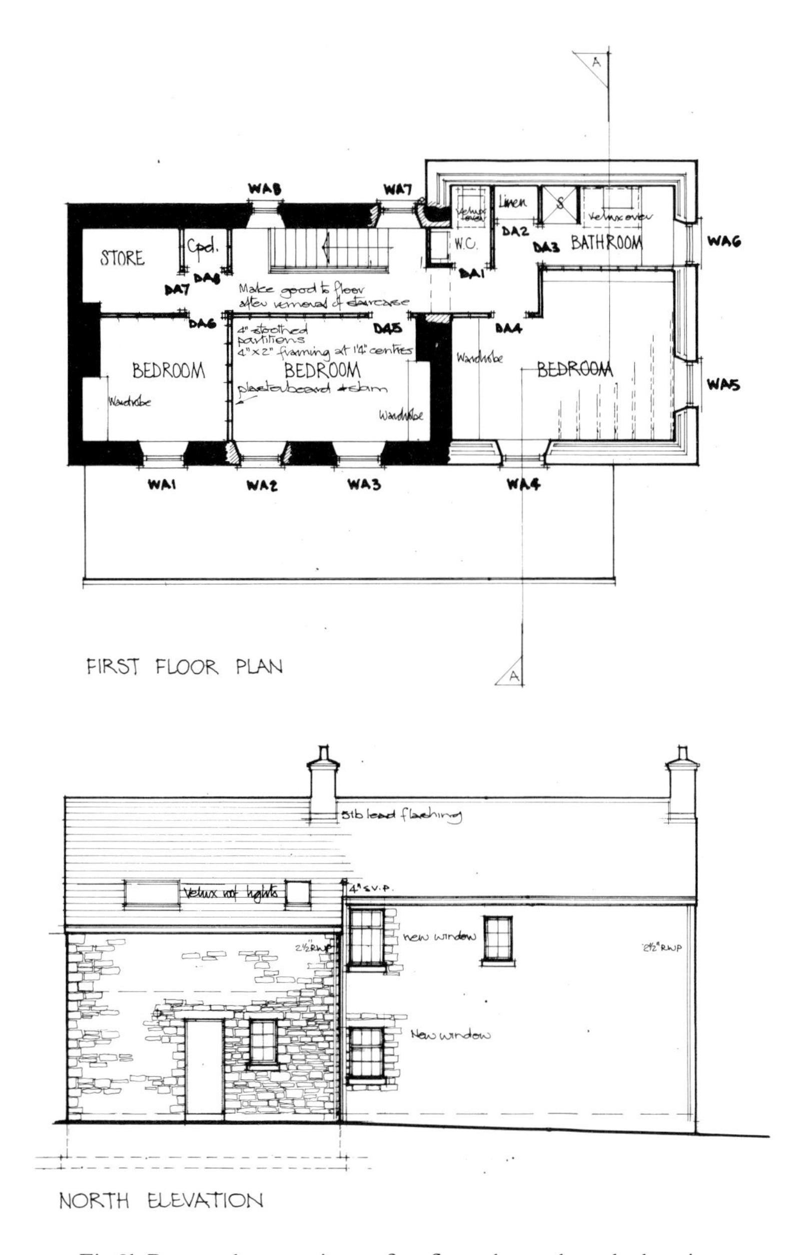

Fig 9b Proposed conversion — first floor plan and north elevation

the various elevations (Figs 9a, 9b, 9c), a section (Fig 9c) (the location of which must be indicated on the floor plans) and a location plan, showing the property in relation to the surroundings. The location plan is generally drawn to a scale of 1:1250, the others are all drawn to a larger scale — generally 1:100. The scale used must be stated on the drawings. Existing work and new work must be clearly distinguished. For the wall structure this is done by infilling the original with solid shading.

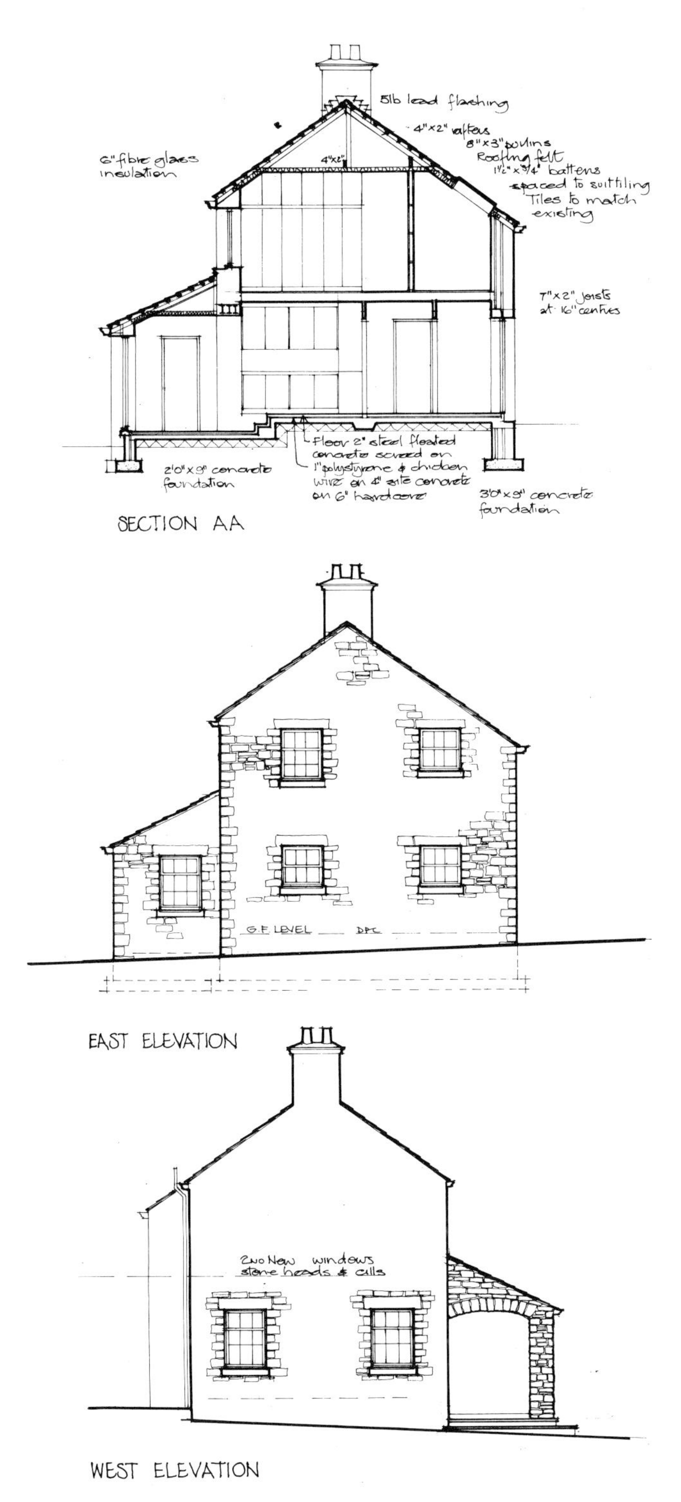

Fig 9c Proposed conversion — section and end elevations

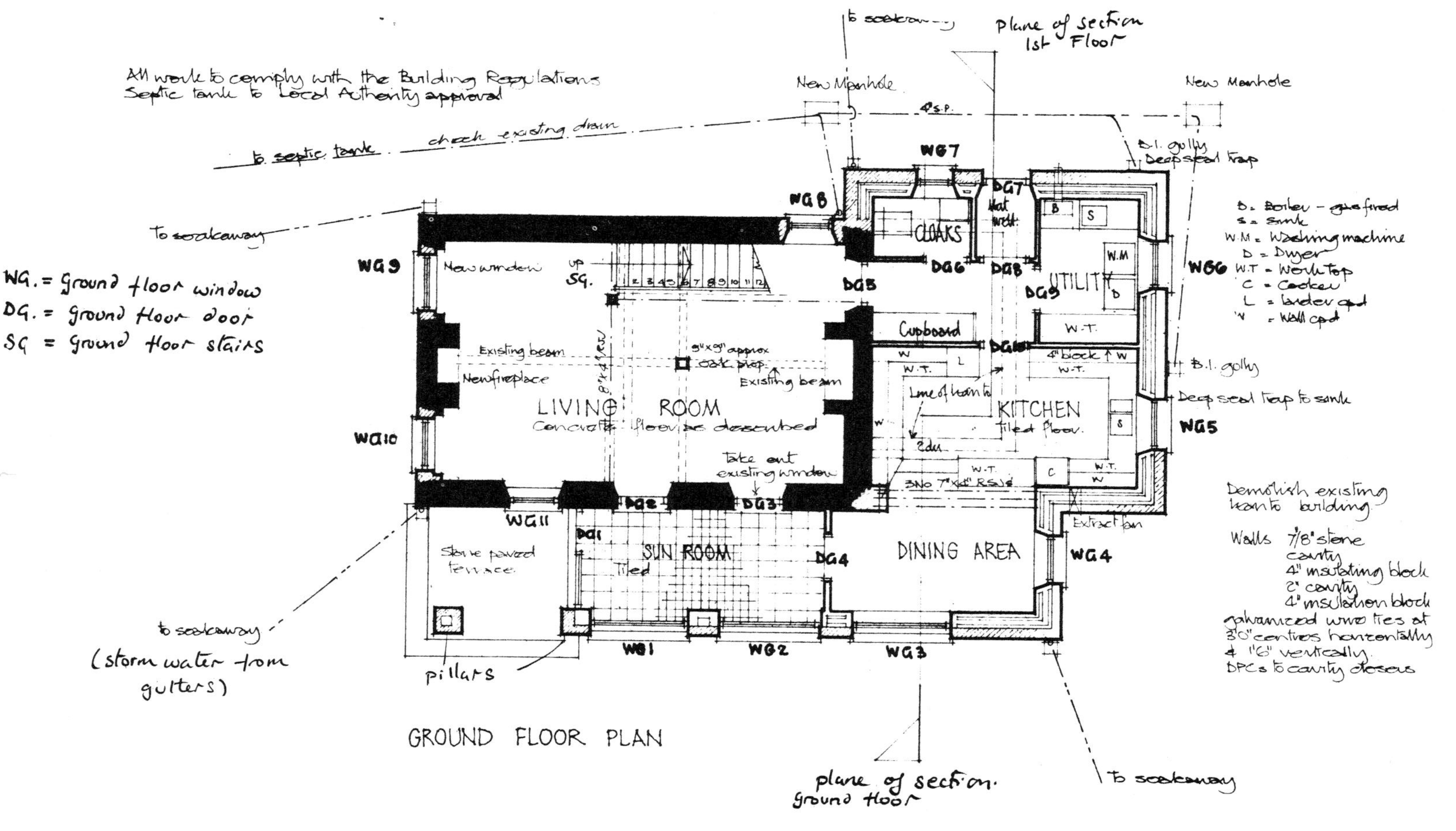

Fig 10 Proposed extension — further detail of ground floor plan

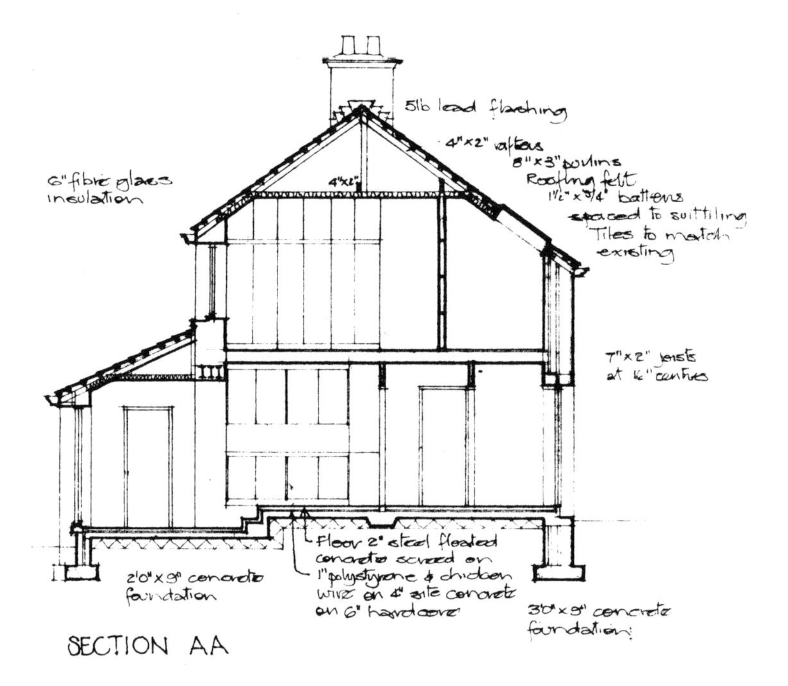

Fig 11 Proposed conversion — section

Many people seem to have considerable difficulty in interpreting plans, somehow lacking the facility to convert a two-dimensional representation into three-dimensional terms. The following approach to the interpretation of drawings may help. Below the ground floor plan will be an elevation which is orientated in exactly the same manner as the ground floor plan. The elevation is really a view of the building as it will look from one side when completed. Start with this picture, identify all the features on it and try to hold an impression of it in your mind. Then locate the doorway or entrance and, if you move directly above this on to the ground floor plan, you will know where you are.

The next stage is to imagine that you are standing at the entrance and, using a pencil on the plan as a marker, take yourself through every room on the ground floor as laid out in the plans. Take your time as you would if you were really walking around the completed building. Hang up your coat (where?), go over to the windows and look out (what's the view like?), put another log on the fire (where are they kept?). When you have finished downstairs walk up the stairs and repeat the same procedure, thinking all the time that you are in the house. All the family are getting up — are the bathroom and toilet facilities adequate? As a housewife, will you have to walk through half the house to transfer the washing from downstairs to the linen cupboard? Would it be better resited?

This may sound silly, but not only will you form an excellent mental impression of what the place is going to look like, you may also discover that certain features of the design are not, after all, to your satisfaction.

JOINERY

Timber

A Softwood is to be sound, dry, well seasoned and square edge redwood or Douglas Fir, merchantable quality. It shall be free from sap, shakes, cracks and loose or dead knots over 1¼″ diameter and the maximum diameter of any knot must not exceed one half of the width of the member.
Hardwoods are to be of prime quality.

Workmanship

B Workmanship is generally to be to BS1186.

Finished faces of joinery

C All surfaces of joinery are to be wrought and then finished with glass paper to remove tool marks. Arrises are to be slightly rounded.
In all work to be painted, all nail heads shall be punched below the surface and filled with lead paste filler for external work and leadless paste filler for internal work.

Mitres

D Rates for joinery shall include all mitres, ends, scribing, fitting and other items to both hardwood and softwood members.

Plugging for joinery

E The rates for joinery are to include for plugging to brickwork, block or concrete where necessary.
Where joinery requires to be plugged, wood plugs shall be provided at not more than 1′ 6″ centres.

Attendance

F The joiner is to attend upon the glazier in fixing wood glazing beads and include in his rates for taking off and refixing.

Storage of joinery

All joinery is to be protected from dampness after delivery to the site. Manufactured joinery is to be primed at the works or immediately upon delivery to the site.

Who wants to be woken at night by the sound of the loo flushing on the other side of a thin partition wall? You might well be if you do not take this mental trip through the plans.

The specification which accompanies the architect's drawings is presented to a standard format but, since it is prepared for an individual undertaking, is not typed on a standard form. The work to be carried out is described not in the order in which it will be done but according to trades, and will be broken down under headings such as concreting, stonework, blockwork and brickwork and carpentry. The specification details the materials to be used and the standard of workmanship required; it does not provide information on quantities needed for a particular project.

The specification is the major protection for any client employing a builder since, having accepted the contract with the specification, the work must be carried out in accordance with its directions. Failure to do so is sound reason for withholding payment to the builder.

One sheet from a specification is reproduced on the facing page as an example of layout and the detail required.

4

Materials

This chapter does not set out to provide a comprehensive list of all the materials required for the job since these will vary widely according to whether you are undertaking a fairly simple renovation or a complex extension project. Such lists are provided by the bill of quantities and specification dealt with in Chapters 2 and 3.

If employing an architect and a builder, obtaining the materials will not concern you, but choosing them will. So be prepared to take an active role at this stage. If the property is brick then insist that any extension is built in matching or compatible brick. If you are using stone, build in similar stone, not some contrasting material or, even worse, an artificial product purporting to be 'indistinguishable from stone'. Should stone prove impossible to obtain then be prepared to render or rough-cast the whole property to achieve continuity. Do not be persuaded by the builder to use materials that he already has in stock and wants to use up, and do not mix materials and styles — the effect can be disastrous (*see* Plates 6 and 7).

If you are undertaking the work yourself, or employing subcontracted labour, then responsibility for the materials will be yours. Remember to check that the contractors are used to working with materials you intend to provide. It is of prime importance, whether using new or reclaimed material, not to under order but to ensure that you have ample for the complete job. It may not be possible to obtain an exact match if a further order has to be made at a later date. I discovered this the hard way during the change from imperial to metric standards: having underestimated the number of 9in quarry tiles I would need for a particular job I was horrified to discover later that only the new metric equivalents were available. It took me far longer to cut these slightly larger tiles down to size than to do the whole of the tiling.

Stone

Since this book is mainly concerned with the renovation of old stone buildings, the most important basic material is stone. The basic types

(Opposite above) Plate 6 Mixing materials and styles has destroyed the character of this old Lake District building. *(Below)* Plate 7 This mixture of types of stone and the general design and appearance produces neither an original effect nor an attractive modern home.

(Left) Plate 8 A ruined and abandoned field barn — a most prized source of materials for the stoneworker. *(Right)* Plate 9 An excellent supply of quoin stones

and origins of building stone have been outlined in Chapter I so they will not be discussed further here.

Obtaining Matching Stone

These days obtaining matching stone for the renovation or extension of an old house or cottage can be quite a problem. Few builders' suppliers deal in stone and you will probably have to look around for it yourself. Only if you are lucky enough to live in an area where stone is still quarried for building purposes, such as North Yorkshire and the Cotswolds, are you likely to be able to order it through the normal channels.

Old property was often built of stone because this was once the cheapest and most readily available building material. It had to be gathered and loaded by hand and would have been transported by horse and cart to the building site. The stone in your cottage most likely came from the immediate locality and similar suitable stone will probably still be there. The main problem is one of accessibility. In upland areas the stone was often scattered naturally over the land and collected to clear and enclose fields and to build shelters, barns and dwellings. Even now in rural areas heaps of cleared, unwanted stone are to be found in fields around farms. These can be bought directly from the farmer, who may be only too pleased to get rid of them.

Similarly, old farm outbuildings are often made redundant by modern farming methods and are either abandoned or demolished in favour of new purpose-built units. But such structures are of the greatest value to the stoneworker and worth a good sum. (Consider the barns shown in Plates 8 and 9.) This is because the stone will have been selected already as suitable for building and will contain a good supply of quoins for corners, ends and openings as well as flat-faced stone for general work. The stone is also likely to match that of your house if it is in the same locality and it will be already weathered. New stone, even if obtained from the same quarry as the original, will look 'new' for many years until the elements have completed their weathering process

If you are lucky enough to become the owner of one of these derelict outbuildings, think twice before you call in a demolition contractor. If you do not want it reduced to a heap of rubble, shovelled up with a mechanical loader and dumped outside your front door, do it yourself; and do it systematically. Start with the roof and work progressively downwards, sorting the stone into separate piles of quoins, flats, and keys as you go. Not only will this save trouble later but you will be able to see how the original building was put together and this will help you when rebuilding your own property.

It is important to save and stack separately all the materials for later use or final disposal, including slates, tiles, timbers and floor slabs even though you may be concerned primarily with the walling stone. When only the walls are left standing resist the temptation to raze them with a sledge-hammer. If you carefully lever off the stone, working round the building in layers, you will avoid shattering good stone and it will be cleaner with less old mortar to scrape off later. If there is no rush to remove the building from its site, take down the stone as you need it instead of all at once. There will be no risk then of using up all the most regularly-shaped stone at the beginning and being left to struggle with the more awkward and irregularly-shaped pieces towards the end. Another advantage is that there will be no need to store heaps of random stone, which cannot be stacked regularly and take up a lot of space.

Most stone hunters will not be lucky enough to find a convenient dilapidated farm building, but there are other sources of stone. If there are several local buildings of the same stone as yours it is almost certain there was once a small quarry in the area. A large scale Ordnance Survey map will show its position. Even if disused there is certain to be plenty of loose stone around suitable for building. If permission to use it is obtained from the owner of the quarry, it can provide an inexhaustible supply for all your needs. Beware, however, not only of the physical dangers of quarrying stone but also the legal ones. Do not automatically assume that the owner of the surrounding land has quarrying rights — these may be held by a third party and you will have to take this into consideration before removing materials.

Working quarries still exist though their modern function is mainly to provide road materials rather than building stone. In any case they are few and far between. It is sometimes possible to obtain walling stone from these works if you make a specific request; and it is worth visiting the quarry with a sample of your own stone to check for a match before you order. The quarrymen will probably be delighted to help you and

Plate 10 Fine examples of urban ashlar work in Harrogate Town Centre. Compare the renovated stonework over the bank with the adjacent building, as yet uncleaned.

offer you all sorts of useful information and advice about working with stone and estimating the right quantity.

It is much more difficult, of course, to obtain good quality stone in urban and semi-urban areas. The wholesale demolition of town centres in the last quarter of a century, in favour of concrete, glass and steel commercial blocks, should have provided ample stone for private housing, from first class ashlar to random rubble, for the next hundred years. Instead, beautiful worked stone has been blasted to pieces and buried — all wasted for the sake of a transient and unnatural architectural fashion. Happily there are signs of this trend reversing and old buildings are beginning to be restored, as in Harrogate town centre in North Yorkshire (Plate 10). More and more councils are, rather belatedly, recognising the value of old stone and it is worth making a direct approach to the appropriate department in your area to see if they could make some available.

If this fails, demolition contractors are another possible source. They are usually paid to demolish and clear a site and anything they make on top of this by tipping a few loads on your doorstep instead of in the dump is additional profit. However, you may have to wait a while until a suitable building is due for demolition and you must expect the load to include a high proportion of undesirable rubbish. Large firms hiring out skips for refuse disposal often have their own dumps and these can

(Above) Plate 11 Lake District stone–work with some unusual features. Note the circular chimney stacks.
(Right) Plate 12 Typical Lake District slate walling showing the deeply raked out joints

occasionally yield a good supply of stone. Yet another possibility is to approach the Church Commissioners to see if they have any old stone properties in your area which they might be willing to sell.

In looking for stone, use your ingenuity, be patient and exhaust every possibility before giving up. The obvious solution may be staring you in the face, as a tale told to me by an old mason in South Wales will illustrate. This mason was employed, by a somewhat impatient client of considerable means, to build a stone extension to an old rural cottage. Matching stone was not readily available so, money being no object, the client bought another cottage, built from similar stone, and instructed the mason to take whatever he required from that. Upon completion of the work — which greatly pleased both parties — the mason was asked if he would undertake one final small job. This was to take down a natural stone wall, which was 6ft (2m) high and ran for 70yd (70m) along one boundary of the property, and dispose of the stone however he could so that a fuchsia hedge could be planted in its place. The stone would have been a perfect match — not that the mason complained, he was able to use it to build several further extensions in the area.

Estimating Quantity of Material Required

The amount of stone required for walling is a function of the area of each stone exposed on the finished surface of the construction. The tonnage of stone required to produce a unit area of facework will vary according to both the basic nature of the stone and the building style adopted. Narrow, flat stones such as the slates used for walling in the Lake District and the sheets of mountain limestone found in the high Pennines lie regularly on top of each other exposing only a small surface area, their bulk being hidden within the wall (Fig 1b and Plates 11 and 12). A great weight of stone is required for each square metre of wall face. In contrast, the 'block' types of stone such as millstone grit, lowland limestone, agglomerates and granites present a larger surface area in relation to their volume and, consequently, less total weight is required to produce a square metre of finished facework (Fig 1c, 2a and Plate 8). At the extreme end of the scale, thin sheets of stone cladded on to blockwork like vertical paving cover a very large area for relatively little weight (Plate 6).

Building style also affects the amount of stone required, different masons producing different areas of facework with the same quantity of stone. This is because, unless working with ashlar, most stones provide a choice of flat surfaces which are very different in area. One stoneworker may favour the largest surface for the face, another will use the smaller surfaces, preferring to leave more bulk within the wall (Fig 1). Over a large area this can cause considerable differences in the total tonnage of walling stone required for the job. The experienced mason usually finds a home for every piece of stone he picks up; you can tell the inexperienced worker by the pile of discards around his feet! Eventually the novice gets rid of this heap of potentially valuable stone as backfill which contributes nothing to the finished wall area, whereas the mason uses almost everything that *is* usable in the face. So it is worth bearing in mind that a good mason will obtain a much larger area of facework from the same amount of stone than somebody, like a bricklayer, who is inexperienced with stone.

Having no doubt just convinced you of the total impossibility of calculating the amount of stone you are going to require for the job, I shall now attempt to explain how you can do just that — and to a fair degree of accuracy.

First you must judge the predominant shape of the stone you are going to use and assign the load as a whole to one of five classes. These classes are:

1 Fairly regular thin sheets of stone which must be laid flat one upon another, for example the slates of North Wales and the Lake District (Plate 13).
2 Irregular thinnish sheets of stone with a small quantity of 'blockier' stone, as in the mountain limestones of the Pennines (Plate 14).
3 Fully random natural stone with fairly even proportions of stone of all shapes and sizes, such as lowland limestones, quarried stone, reclaimed stone, field gathered stone, Ice Age moraine stone, granites, etc (Plate 15).
4 Partly random stone with a high proportion of regular blocks, for example millstone grits, Forest of Dean and other sandstones and reclaimed stone from old urban constructions (*see* Plate 2).
5 Fully regular stone such as ashlar and dressed, cut stones generally only occurring in localised areas, such as Bath stone, Portland stone.

Having classified the stone you must then classify yourself as the stoneworker. First consider just how experienced you are with stone; bricklaying is not the same and will place you quite definitely in the inexperienced class. Then decide which building style you will adopt, whether you are going to favour a large face for the individual stones with little bulk in the wall and use a lot of rubble for backfill, or expose the smaller faces leaving more bulk to tie-in within the wall (Fig 12).

Once you have classified both yourself and the stone consult the table in Fig 13 and read off at the intersection of the two classifications the area in square metres that will be produced in a *single* face by one tonne of stone. For example, the experienced worker using fully random stone and adopting the 'large-face' building style, will produce approximately 2.8 square metres of facework for every tonne of stone supplied.

To calculate the total tonnage needed for a job is simply a matter of calculating the total area of the facework to be produced from your scale plans, making allowances for hidden work, chimney stacks, returns etc., and dividing this total area by the figure obtained from the table.

Plate 13 A renovated slate barn with string courses and massive quoins

Plate 14 An abandoned mountain limestone building

Plate 15 A renovated cottage in South Wales showing random stonework and wooden lintels

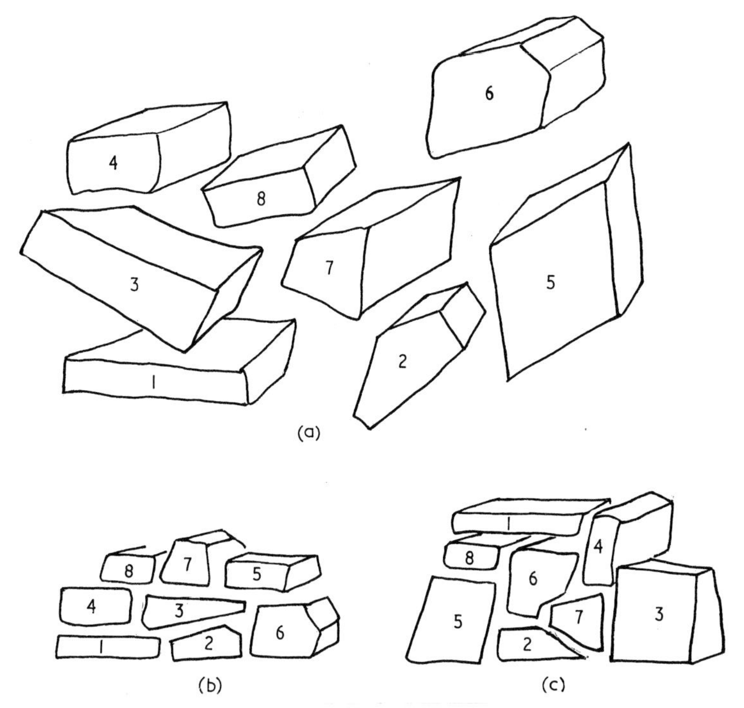

Fig 12 (a) A selection of random-shaped building stone; (b) the stone laid flat, producing a small area of facework; (c) an alternative method of laying the same stone to produce a larger area of facework

From experience I have found the best way to do this is to ignore all windows and doors on the plans and calculate the total wall area as if they were not there. Not only do you save yourself a lot of arithmetic but this larger figure allows for hidden work and general wastage, to provide a margin of safety against under ordering. The wall area for the extension shown in Fig 9 using stone only on the exterior and blocks on the internal wall would be $90m^2$ and the hypothetical stoneworker previously described would need 32 tonnes of fully randomised stone.

Sorting and Storing

Loose stone takes up a tremendous amount of space and some consideration should be given to where it can be stored following delivery. Remember that stone will be used throughout the whole of the building work and so must be placed where it is constantly available. It is best to sort and place the stone where it is going to be most accessible, as soon as it is delivered.

With any extension or renovation work there will always be ends, corners and openings which require turning the facework through a right angle. Special stones termed *quoins*, which have two faces at right angles to each other (Fig 14) are required to accomplish this. All quoins should be separated from the bulk of stone and placed in heaps convenient to the corners of the proposed extension. As there is inevitably a

Approximate area of facework (m^2) built per tonne

Stone classification	Experienced with stone: Large face style	Experienced with stone: Small face style	Inexperienced with stone: Large face style	Inexperienced with stone: Small face style
1 Regular thin sheets eg slates	2.2	2.2	2.0	2.0
2 Thinnish sheets with some block eg mountain limestone	2.5	2.4	2.3	2.1
3 Fully random field stone	2.8	2.6	2.5	2.3
4 Regular blocks with some random eg millstone grits	3.3	3.0	3.0	2.8
5 Fully regular eg Bath stone	3.5	3.5	3.4	3.4

Fig 13 A guide to the area of facework produced per tonne of stone

shortage of such quoins, unless using dressed or semi-dressed stone, any stone with anything like a square edge, whether tall and thin or short and fat, should be consigned to these piles. On no account, and this is particularly stressed for beginners, should any of this stone be used in the bulk of the walling, otherwise you will end up having to waste time and energy cutting stone into quoins long before the facework has reached the level of the first floor joists.

Make separate piles of very large stones, either in block form or of a paving shape: these will be important as *tie* stones and *uprights* (*see* Chapters 6 and 7). These piles should be centred on the run of the proposed walls but placed well back out of the way. Also, having to go and collect these stones at regular intervals ensures that the stoneworker frequently views the whole construction from a distance as work progresses and can thus maintain continuity of style. The bulk of the building stone should not be graded for either shape or size. This prevents areas

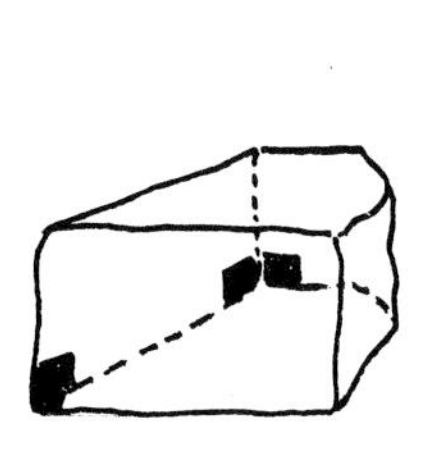
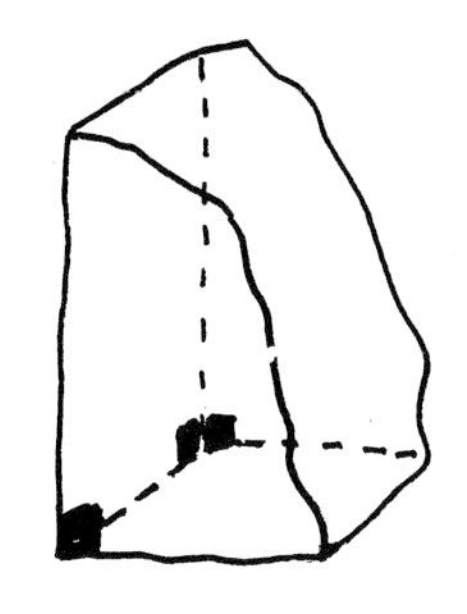
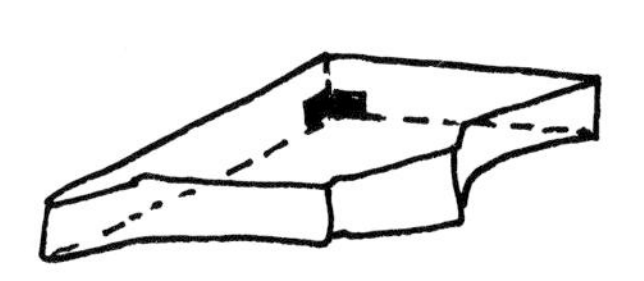

Fig 14 Some useful shapes for quoin stones — the right-angles are shaded

of variation in the finished job. Instead it should be barrowed in as it comes and placed in heaps around the building close to hand. Remember to leave several points of access to barrow in other materials. Finally, heap together rubble, dust and chips of stone on a hard surface so that it is easy to shovel when you need infill for cavities later.

Special stones, such as those selected for sills or lintels, or polished slates for floors should be stored under cover and protected with sacking or old matting until they are required. This prevents them from inadvertently becoming stained, scratched or broken before they can be used. They could prove both difficult and expensive to replace.

Blocks and Bricks

Even when building in stone, blocks and bricks will always be required for certain aspects of the work. If the internal walls are going to be plastered, papered or painted it is senseless to build such walls of stone. Similarly, partition walls which bear a load are easier to construct and have less bulk when built from blocks than from stone.

Blocks

Since the external skin of the cottage extension is to be built of stone to match the existing dwelling, external heavy duty weather-resistant blocks will not be required: so we are only concerned with lightweight internal blockwork. Numerous blocks of this type are on the market. Provided they satisfy the building regulation requirements as regards thermal insulation, fire resistance and load bearing capacity the choice of block depends upon local availability and personal views. If you are going to sub-contract the internal rendering and plasterwork it is worth consulting the plasterer for his preferences since some blocks do take a render better than others.

All types of blocks are fragile compared with stone and the method of delivery will certainly affect the number of breakages. Try and obtain blocks on pallets that can be off-loaded with a hoist rather than have them tipped off the back of a truck. You are going to break plenty of blocks yourself during the course of building so it is worth at least starting with as many whole ones as possible.

Blocks are purchased by number (usually per hundred), not weight, so amounts required are fairly simple to calculate if one allows 10 per m^2 of finished work. As in the case of stone, calculate the area of walling from the scale plans, then divide this figure by ten to give the number needed. But, if using the cavity method of construction described in Part II, remember to double this figure since there will be *two* internal walls. Special blocks for fireplaces and flues can be bought separately as required.

Bricks

Even if the internal skins are being constructed of blocks, some bricks will be required to bring certain parts of the walling to predetermined levels which may not be an exact block depth. This is particularly important in siting the floor joists and wall-plate to carry the roof as well as over doors and windows where internal lintels are placed. Common bricks are used for this purpose and from experience I have found the 'frogged-common' the best general purpose brick since it can be easily chipped down to produce a narrower unit. This is quite important for the do-it-yourselfer who may not always maintain a perfectly true level in the courses of blockwork and will have to compensate sometimes.

Cottages constructed solely of brick are not really the concern of this book, but the external brickwork of such old dwellings should normally be matched in any extension. This is not easy since old bricks were often hand-thrown and vary in both shape and size in comparison with the uniformity of modern facing bricks. The problems associated with obtaining matching stone may well be echoed in the quest for old bricks. Some brick firms do produce specially textured and weathered brick faces to blend in with old brickwork. A builders' supplier should be able to help find firms from whom samples can be obtained.

Commons are normally quoted as so much per hundred or thousand, it obviously being slightly cheaper to purchase by the thousand. If building basically in block and stone you will not require a vast quantity. However, even a thousand bricks do not go very far so it is best to order at least this number to start with. If more are required later, they can be ordered by the hundred.

Timber

Every joiner I have ever met has complained that timber these days is nowhere near as good as it used to be, but they have to make do with it because it is all they can get. I am not prepared to comment on the quality of timber but would caution the do-it-yourselfer not to set off to the local sawmills or timber merchant expecting to purchase oak and cedar beams and boards. Even if the merchant did stock such wood to suit your DIY ideals, it certainly would not suit your DIY pocket.

The major timber work in cottage renovation and extension will be in the roof, upper floors and partitions, and here the main structural timbers must satisfy Building Regulation Standards, both in the dimensions of individual timbers and their spacing. Such details will be set out in the specification for the building work and using this, together with the scale plans, quantities can be calculated for all horizontal members such as floor joists, wall plates and purlins. Calculating the rafter length, however, is not so easy. You can either utilize the end elevation on the scale drawing, or treat the roof as a right-angled triangle in section from the eaves to the ridge and calculate the rafters (the hypotenuse) directly by Pythagoras' Theorem (Fig 9c).

If you are going to do the timber work yourself never order to the exact finished lengths required, but allow a margin for error to compensate for incorrectly cut joints or unevenness in the block and stonework. When building by mass construction methods the timberwork has to be fitted to the existing stonework. In old buildings this can vary considerably. If sub-contracting the work to a joiner ask him to calculate his timber requirements, check them yourself to ensure that he is not over-ordering for his own purposes, and order accordingly.

Do not store wood outside but keep it dry under cover to prevent warping. It is better laid flat with battens between to allow free circulation of air, rather than leant against a wall. If possible obtain timber that has been pre-treated against rot which, though more expensive, can save time and effort on proofing it yourself.

For those fortunate enough to have found an old barn or demolished building, the original timbers may still be usable. These are quite likely to be hardwood and superficial damage should not automatically consign them to the fire heap. Woodworm holes in a large beam are unlikely to mean that the whole beam is unsound. Generally penetration is little more than a few millimetres from the surface. The affected part can be adzed off (*see* Chapter 10) and the remaining wood then treated to

Plate 16 An old beam with extensive internal damage by dry rot *Rentokil Ltd*

prevent re-infection. Similarly, rot may be confined to the ends where timbers were inserted into stonework and became damp. If these rotten ends are sawn off the remaining length of sound wood can be re-used. It is most unwise, however, to re-use timber that has been infected with dry rot (Plate 16). This is caused by a fungus with particularly resistant spores which can rapidly infect and damage new timber.

Apart from timber used directly in the construction of the property, odd lengths are always required for props, formwork, and guides. The temptation is to go to the wood store and cut off a new piece as it is needed. It is better instead to over order and set some lengths aside specifically for these odd requirements and not mix them up with the constructional timber.

Windows and Doors

The types of windows and doors used is of course a matter of personal choice, but regardless of whether these are being custom built or factory made, do not start on the walling until they have been delivered. It is far easier to build the returns of the openings with the frames in place than to have to fit the frames into pre-built openings, however careful you have been with your measurements.

The frames should also be primed to protect the wood from the weather during the building period. Factory frames are usually ready primed for you, but custom frames are often not, and should be given this important protection immediately they are delivered.

Store all frames in the dry with the windows fastened and the door frames held rigid with a cross batten to prevent distortion.

Sand, Aggregate and Cement

If you are embarking on a major building project, it is cheaper and easier to have your sand delivered by the lorry load to the site, replenishing the stock as required. This ideally should be tipped onto a clean, prepared hard surface within easy barrowing distance of the building work. It is not a good idea to have it too close. Ten tonnes of sand piled against the building is a nuisance not only to access but also because the facework will inevitably become stained and disfigured when making the mixes.

To minimise loss sand should be kept heaped up and not allowed to spread around. An extra precaution is to cover the pile with a sheet when not in use to stop the considerable losses that can occur in high winds and heavy rainfall. Concrete aggregate should be placed adjacent to, but separate from, the building sand. Pebbles in a walling mix are not only a nuisance when bedding blocks and stones but can mar the joints in the completed facework.

Cement deteriorates from the moment it is made, so it should not be stored in vast quantities. Never order more than half a ton at a time, except for foundation and floor concrete, and keep the bags in a dry shed or empty room clear of the floor. Try to use up a whole number of bags at each session to prevent working with half used bags that may have stood around for some time after being opened. Never use old cement that has started to become lumpy and brittle — it will produce an unsatisfactory mortar with very poor bonding properties.

Roofing Materials

The materials used for covering the roofs of old buildings are at least as variable as those employed in the walls. All were dependent upon local availability in the past and all are equally difficult to match in modern times.

Thatch

Thatch was probably the most universal roof covering originally used in Britain. The main materials were reeds, which were specially cultivated in lowland areas such as Norfolk, wheat straw, in agricultural districts, and heather, in upland areas where straw was scarce. Although thatch still remains, it has been extensively replaced by more durable materials. With the shortage of skilled thatchers plus the expense of maintaining thatch in good condition the decline seems certain to continue.

If purchasing an old thatched cottage it may be worth considering the complete removal of the thatch if in poor condition and its replacement by slates or tiles. As well as being virtually maintenance free, these are less of a fire risk. Do, however, be certain that the roof timbers are adequate to carry the increased load, since thatch is an extremely light roofing material.

Slate

Slate as a roofing material was originally restricted to those regions where slate occurred naturally, such as the Lake District, North and West Wales, Devon and Cornwall, Leicestershire and the Isle of Man. The rapid expansion of rail transport at the end of the nineteenth century led to the use of Welsh slate throughout the country as a substitute for thatch. Such slate is usually used in the form of very thin sheets of uniform size and thickness, except ironically in Wales where less uniformity is encountered, the best slates being exported to England. The other types of slate are found in random widths and thicknesses (Plates 17 and 18) and are laid in irregular diminishing courses. All slates are generally 'hung' on nails driven into battens or laths which are attached at appropriate spacings on the rafters. They have the advantage of being relatively light, extremely waterproof and of being suitable for a wide range of roof pitches.

Unfortunately under competition from cheaper, mass produced, man-made materials, very little roofing slate is mined these days and the great slate quarries of Wales remain virtually idle. However, since slates were once so widely used, and are simple to remove and to store, stocks of second-hand Welsh slates can still be obtained without too much difficulty from builders' merchants, building contractors and demolition firms. Do, however, check the merchandise before purchase and pay particular attention to the region around the nail holes since this is an area of weakness. Reject slates where this hole has been greatly enlarged, or where the surround looks flakey and also those with hairline cracks.

It is worth stressing also that, should *you* be replacing a slate roof with some other material, somebody somewhere will be happy to buy your sound second hand slates. So remove them carefully and advertise them in the local paper. I have a cautionary tale for those employing a builder or roofing contractor to replace the slates: such firms generally regard these 'demolition materials' as a perk of the job without any right to do so. Friends of mine who refused permission for the builders to remove the slates from the site returned from holiday to find every slate had been thrown from the roof to the ground and were lying smashed all round the house. Make sure your contract states that the roofing materials are to be removed in good condition and stacked, or do it yourself. The slates on re-sale could be worth several hundred pounds.

Stone Flags and Stone Tiles

Stone used as a roofing material is mainly confined to old buildings in areas where the naturally occurring stone is of the sort that can be split into broad thin sheets. Even so these will be of two basic types: stone flags, which tend to be fairly thick, heavy and rather irregular in outline (as found in the Pennines, *see* Plates 5 and 9) and stone tiles, which are thinner and more regular (as seen in the Cotswolds). Flags are generally cut from sandstone and tiles from limestone but, regardless of origin, the method of laying is similar. So is the basic unit shape (Fig 15) with both tiles and flags being roughly shaped at the apex and held on battens by a single peg, originally made from oak or even bone. Stone flags are generally restricted to a low pitch of no more than 30° whereas the lighter tiles could be hung onto roof pitches of up to 50°.

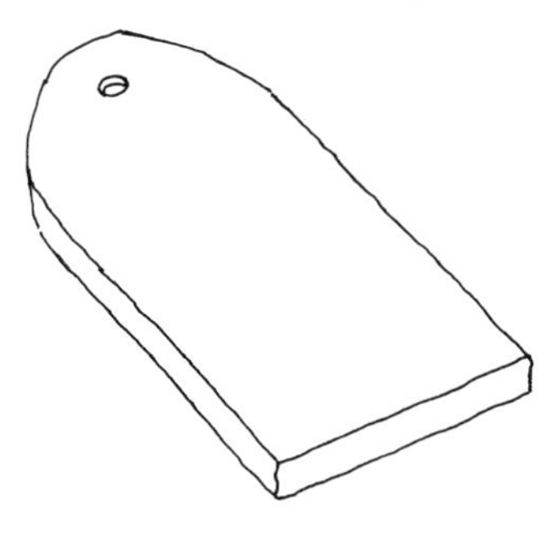

Fig 15 An old stone roofing flag. (Also known as stone slates in the North of England)

(*Above*) Plate 17 A pile of old Westmorland roofing slates showing their irregular size.
(*Below*) Plate 18 Westmorland slate roof laid in diminishing courses

Stone flags are no longer produced and can only be obtained from demolished buildings. Their weight necessitates a fairly massive timber support and they are less waterproof than slates or modern tiles. Most second hand material is damaged and watersoaked and, except in special circumstances, I would recommend their removal from an old dwelling and replacement with lighter clay tiles.

Stone tiles, though expensive, are still produced to satisfy planning requirements in Cotswold villages and in such areas a person renovating an old dwelling will be required to use this traditional roofing material.

Clay Tiles

Clay tiles and bricks have been produced since the fifteenth century. Their use was initially confined to East Anglia and Southern England where stone and slate were not available, but they soon spread throughout the country with the growth of urbanisation, industrialisation, mass production and distribution. Man-made tiles, whether of clay, cement or other more modern material, are used for the majority of roofing jobs today.

Clay tiles are of two types: plain tiles, which are very slightly curved and hung onto battens by means of nibs moulded into the tiles and nails (Fig 16), or pantiles, which are of a stretched S-shape in cross section (Fig 17). Both plain tiles and pantiles have standard dimensions and are regular in form unlike slate and stone roofing materials.

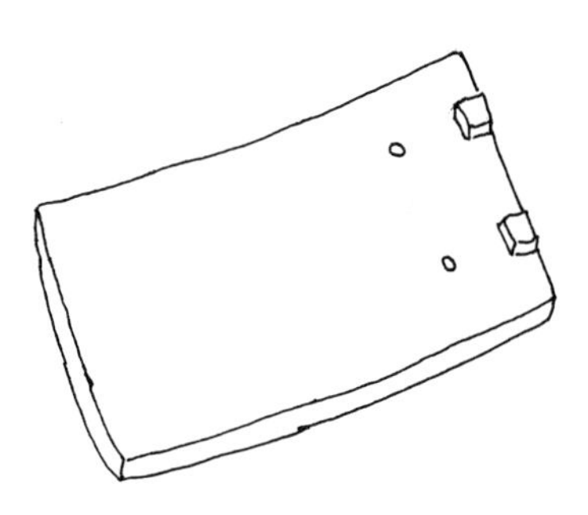

Fig 16 A plain clay tile viewed from the underside

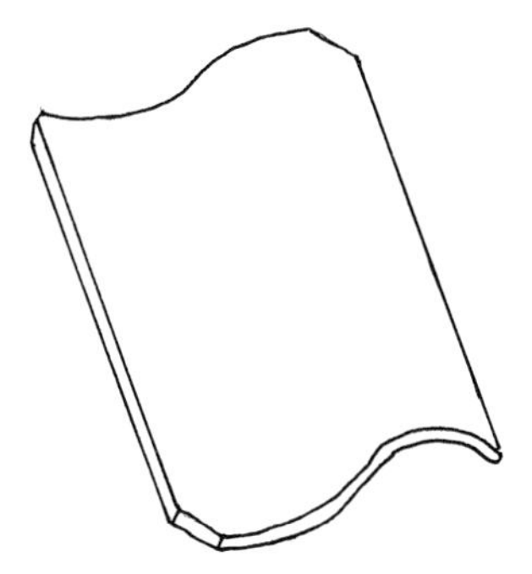

Fig 17 A clay pantile

Plain tiles are usually laid at a pitch of more than 45° and, because they can be specially moulded, they can satisfy a variety of roof shapes. They are laid in regular courses with one tile overlapping the joint between two tiles beneath, hence a relatively small area of the individual tile is exposed on the finished roof.

Pantiles, although made from similar materials, are used rather differently. Each tile laps only one tile beneath so that a greater proportion of each tile is exposed on the finished roof. Consequently they provide a relatively lightweight roof and can be laid to low pitches of 30° to 35°.

Plate 19 A modern housing estate in the Yorkshire Dales keeping to traditional materials and methods

Both plain tiles and pantiles are still manufactured and there should be little problem in matching roof materials for an extension requiring this type of material (Plate 19). Pantiles, though common throughout the Eastern counties of Britain from London to Scotland, are rarely seen in the West of England.

Modern Tiles

There is a vast range of modern roofing tiles available and I do not intend to discuss the various types individually. However, there are a few general rules to follow which apply to them all. You should never mix modern materials with old. Either stick to the old or replace the lot with new tiles to ensure continuity. Choose a tile suitable for the pitch of the roof concerned — if there are several roofs of different pitches to be tackled on the same dwelling, be certain that the tile you select is suitable for them all. Modern multi-coloured tiles do not suit old buildings, a much more natural effect is obtained by allowing the tiles to weather in their own good time.

Introduction

Before going into the purely practical aspects of extension and renovation, it is worth pointing out a few of the problems likely to occur.

With simple renovation work the main problems are generally encountered in obtaining matching materials in an age where everything has become standardised. Even just replacing a rotten window frame or broken floor tile may involve considerable time and expense.

In an old stone building nothing will be standard and very little perfectly straight or square. Beware of factory produced, ready-to-assemble, fitted kitchen units. These are designed for the modern home and the odds are against them 'fitting' in your old rural one. And what might initially seem to be a minor undertaking such as the erection of a couple of shelves on brackets could turn out to be a rather demanding project requiring the shaping of the shelf back to accommodate irregularities in the wall, a percussion drill to make the holes in a particularly hard chunk of stone and endless patience. Adopt the approach that it is going to be more difficult than it looks and will take twice as long as you expect. Then you will get a chance to enjoy doing it.

A modern house has perhaps twenty or more different electrical appliances, many of which are situated in the kitchen and often operated simultaneously. An old rural cottage generally has very few plug sockets and those it has are likely to have been added as the need arose over the years and be of various types. The temptation is to opt for a cheap solution and purchase a number of adaptors to both standardise the sockets throughout the home and increase the number of appliances that may be run from a single socket. However, at best this solution leads to overloading and blown fuses, at worst it could cause a serious fire. If the wiring is more than twenty years old you would be well advised to have the whole place re-wired. Not only will your home be safer but you will be able to have the sockets you require located where *you* want them.

Very few rural sites are naturally level and for two good reasons it is generally preferable to build the extension on the lower ground wherever possible. Not only is considerable expense saved by avoiding having to dig out the higher ground, particularly if it happens to be rock, but it also overcomes some problems encountered as a result of regulations concerning the height of ceilings. In the original building the ceilings are likely to be lower than the regulation minimum, but the extension will have to comply with this minimum. In a two storey extension therefore, unless the ground floor begins at a lower level, the new ridge will be higher than that on the original cottage (if the roofs are to have the same pitch). Building from a lower starting point may solve the problem of getting an even ridge height throughout the dwelling.

The experienced builder and architect will be aware of such problems but the novice do-it-yourselfer may not. If you are going to undertake the building of an extension yourself and have had little previous experience, I would strongly urge that you draw up your plans with the help of an architect.

One area where problems arise is rarely considered in advance, or even recognised until considerable damage has been done. It is that of domestic like and routine. If major renovation work is to be undertaken while you are living in the building then marital relationships are at the very least likely to become strained. If you have children to cope with as well, life could be sheer hell. I can offer little advice on how to minimise the stress. Some people recommend that it is best to get the job done as quickly as possible regardless of the severe inconvenience at the time, others that it should proceed little by little to minimise the disruption.

Chapters 5 to 9 outline the step by step construction of a modest extension to an old stone cottage, although the techniques will be applicable to any stonework renovation. The reader is placed in the role of the small builder concerned with the erection and improvement of the shell of the buildings and it is assumed that the intention is to employ sub-contractors for specific specialist jobs such as electrical work, plumbing and plastering. In the long run such an approach can be as cheap as doing everything yourself since expensive specialist tools will not have to be purchased or hired and the work will be completed far more quickly. However, for the totally dedicated DIY enthusiast, numerous handbooks are available to assist with such specialised work (*see* Bibliography).

By this time all plans should have been passed, the necessary building permission obtained, grant applications made and agreed and local authority cards to notify the building inspector of the progress of the work obtained. For the purpose of this book the project to be tackled is the extension of a basic two-up-and-two-down rural cottage similar to the one shown in the plans in Figs 8–11. (*See also* Plate 1.) The design has assumed occupancy of the cottage whilst the extension is being built and the new construction places thermal insulation high on the list of priorities. The materials are assumed to be on site or at least readily available.

Such a renovation and extension project using the services of an architect and builder would have cost about £2,000 in 1960, £12,000 in 1970 and £25,000 in 1980. Should a similar inflationary trend continue, the costs would approach £40,000 in 1990. By undertaking the work yourself these costs would be at least halved.

5

Foundations and Drains

Foundations

Although the plans indicate the need for considerable demolition work to the original dwelling, it is not necessarily the best way to start. This is particularly important if you are living in the house or cottage which should be kept intact and weatherproof for as long as possible by erecting the extension around it. Leave all demolition work until the last possible moment by taking down only whatever is absolutely necessary to allow the smooth progress of the building work.

The new design illustrated in the plans enables all demolition work to be left until the shell is complete to the first floor joists when the 'lean-to' kitchen addition can be removed. This 'lean-to' was a later addition to the original cottage, built with a mixture of brick and stone, without proper foundations and not 'tied-in' to the cottage. If the cottage is unoccupied I would certainly recommend demolition from the outset, allowing a clear area for unhindered progress and re-use of the demolition materials in the new building. In our case, however, this is the functional kitchen of a home, so demolition work will be delayed until absolutely necessary.

The foundations of a building are designed to spread the load of the whole structure evenly over a large area so that no undue pressure is put on the subsoil at any particular point. They must be strong enough to prevent the load from shearing the foundation itself, must accommodate limited ground movements, be resistant to attack from natural elements, satisfy the statutory requirements of the Building Regulations and meet with the approval of the local building inspector.

The only view on the plans which shows the foundations in detail is the section shown in Fig 9c. Here the portion of the building work which extends below ground level is detailed together with the dimensions of the foundations themselves. Such foundations are termed *strip foundations* and it should also be noted that, owing to the weight of the stone walling construction to be used, these are considerably more massive than those normally used for standard cavity walling in a modern home.

Laying Out

Before marking out, the site should be cleared of all loose debris and surface vegetation, a quantity of stout pointed pegs made and sufficient good quality line purchased. The purpose of laying out is to provide guide lines from which the foundations can be dug and the walls can be erected, and the easiest way to accomplish this is to use profile boards. These are 120cm (4ft) boards to which stout, pointed pegs have been attached which can be firmly driven into the ground (Fig 18). When in position saw cuts are made in the boards to carry the strings marking the exact position of the foundations and walls.

The first step in using these boards is to stretch strings along part of the face of the south and north walls of the cottage and extend these eastwards just beyond the limit of the new extension (Fig 19). By measuring accurately along these two lines the end of the new extension can be determined and a string laid down to mark the position of the east wall (Fig 19). But before the profile boards are knocked in it is very important to check that the corners form exact right angles. This is most easily done by straightforward measurement: the simplest right angled triangle has its sides in the ratio 3:4:5. Thus, measuring from the point where the strings cross, if a point 3m away is marked off on one string

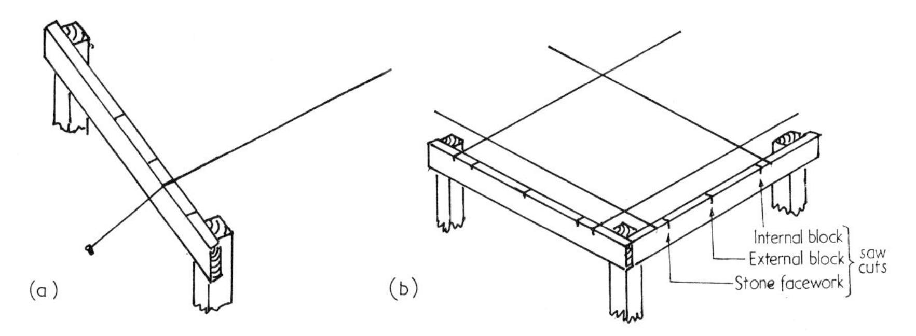

Fig 18 Profile boards: (a) simple profile; (b) corner profile with strings for strip foundations in position

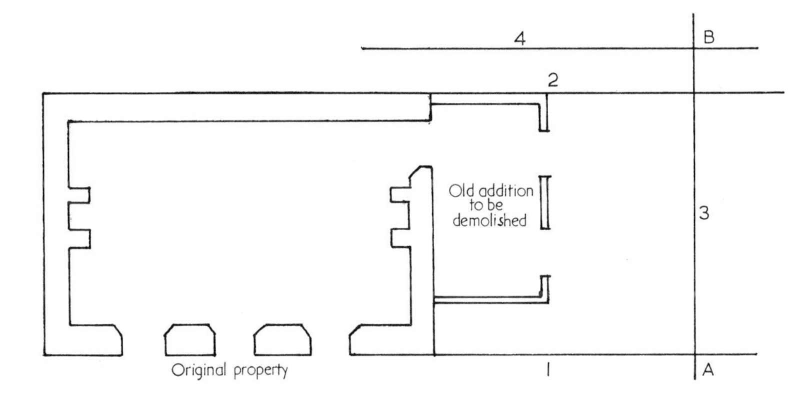

Fig 19 Laying out the position of a new extension. The strings are set out in the order they are numbered (1-4) and mark the positions of the South East (A) and North East (B) corners of the new extension (see text)

and a point 4m away is marked off on the other, then the distance between these two points (the hypotenuse of the right angled triangle) should measure 5m exactly (Fig 20). If it does not, start again. Not until it is exact should you make saw cuts in the profile boards, pass the strings through and anchor them firmly in position.

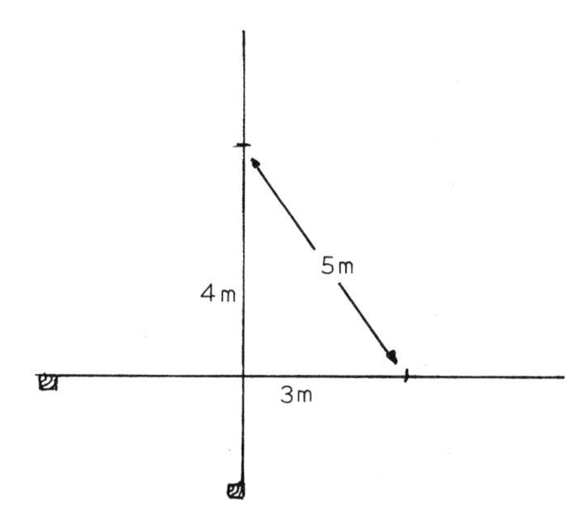

Fig 20 Checking for a right-angle

By measurement the new position of the north wall and the 'lean-to' external south wall can be marked out and checked as above and these profile boards permanently placed (Fig 21). Finally, the line of the remaining internal wall is determined by measurement (Fig 21). What are now marked out on the ground are the positions of the external faces of the walls of the proposed extension, not the line of the foundation trenches. These are directly marked out on the profile boards by measurement from the saw cut carrying the external wall string. Since the foundations exceed the overall wall thickness by 10cm (4in) on each side, a new saw cut is made exactly 10cm to the *outside* of the first cut on each profile board and a new string laid to these cuts. This string marks the outside of each foundation trench. The position of the inside line is determined by measuring inwards from this second cut a distance equal to the total width of the foundation. On this line a third cut is made in the profile boards. The first strings laid (those marking the external wall faces) are now removed and placed in the new cuts as they have served their purpose (Fig 18b).

If you have remembered to keep checking your right angles, the outlines of the foundation trenches should be accurately marked out with the strings. At the same time the position of the outside wall faces have already been marked on the profile boards. Before excavation is started a card must be sent to the local authority so that the marking out can be inspected and permission to continue obtained.

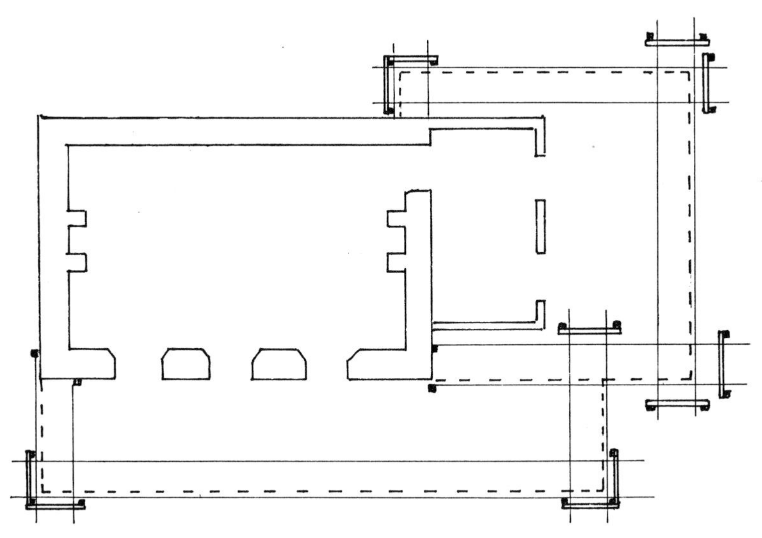

Fig 21 Laying out positions of the strip foundations using pegs and simple and corner profile boards. (Solid lines = strings marking foundation trenches; broken lines = exterior of the proposed extension)

Excavation

Excavation can be either by hand or by mechanical digger which can be hired by the hour complete with operator. The latter is undeniably quicker though obviously very much more expensive. If a pit needs to be dug for a septic tank to be installed then it is probably more sensible to hire a mechanical digger and complete *all* the excavation work in one operation, providing suitable access is available. Otherwise, excavation by hand has numerous benefits, apart from the very practical one of saving money. Excavated material can be graded and transported to where it is required. Also it is the ideal way for people unused to physical work to tone up muscle and harden hands before the actual building work starts, and it is an excellent brake upon wild visions of completing the work in a few weeks. It is also more precise than a digger can ever be.

The first step is to make deep, vertical, spade cuts along the length of the two strings marking each foundation trench to keep the walls of the trench firm and straight. If the area is turfed this should be removed next and either re-laid where needed or composted. Excavation of the topsoil is done by spade and barrow directly to where it is needed or to where it can be stacked for use at a later stage. To prevent mixing of subsoil and topsoil all the topsoil should be removed before starting excavation into the deeper layers. All excavated material should be loaded directly into barrows and carted away. Do not heap the material outside the trench! Not only will this involve an additional loading operation at a later stage, it will also hamper access to the work and will inevitably keep falling back into the trench.

After removing the topsoil, the subsoil should be excavated in successive levels of about a spade depth (this may require a pick and shovel) until the required depth is reached. The subsoil should be carted away, either used in the garden for altering levels, or barrowed into a skip and dumped off-site. When digging it is important to keep the sides of the trenches vertical and when the required depth is reached (remembering always that the finished level of the foundations will be below ground level) the floor of the trench is made level and smooth. No rocks or other obstructions should be left projecting into the trenches.

On sloping sites the trenches and strip foundations will have to be stepped to avoid unnecessary excavations to maintain a true level. Here digging should start at the lowest corner and the trench bottom be maintained at a fixed level for a distance until the surface slope has risen about the depth of a building block. The trench bottom is then stepped up a block's depth and this new level maintained until a further step is necessary (Fig 22). This will not only maintain a constant thickness of concrete throughout the foundations but will also facilitate the continuity of blockwork courses throughout the building. Where stepping is required it will be indicated on the elevations shown in the plans (Figs 8 and 9). Where pillars are to be erected, as with the new south facing 'lean-to', the strip foundations need to be enlarged into pads to carry the increased load (Fig 23).

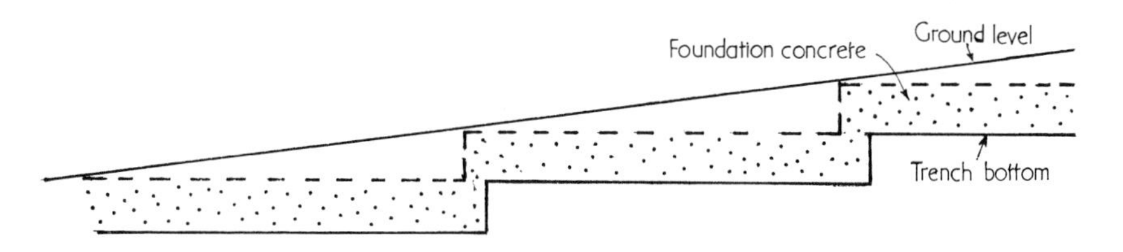

Fig 22 Stepped foundations. For ease of construction each step should be an even number of bricks and mortar joints high so that courses will be level throughout

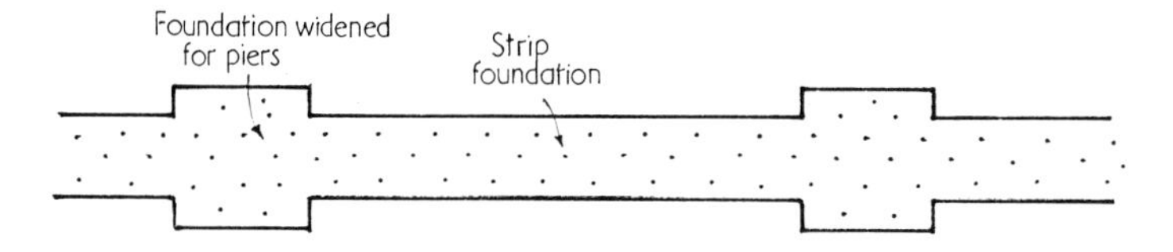

Fig 23 Widening of strip foundations to provide support for piers where these are required

Levelling

When all the trenches have been dug, pegging and levelling can begin. Starting from the lowest corner a peg is driven into the centre of the bottom of the trench until it stands the required height of the foundations within the trench. (For example, if the plans show the foundations to be specified as 45cm deep, the peg should protrude 45cm from the trench bottom.) Further pegs are then placed into the trenches about 3m

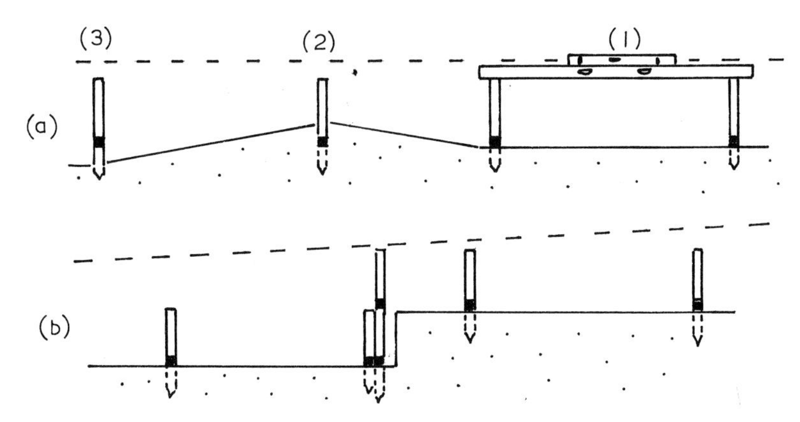

Fig 24 Levelling and checking the depth of foundation trenches: (a) level ground (1) correct depth and level (2) trench too shallow (3) trench too deep; (b) sloping ground with stepped foundations

(approximately 10ft) apart starting from the first peg and levelled off to that peg. This is done using a 'straight edge' and spirit level to level the second peg to the first, third to the second and so on throughout the trenches (Fig 24a). Eventually the tops of all the pegs should be at the same level. Each peg is then checked to see that it stands the required minimum height above the bottom of the trench. If not, the trench bottom is lowered by excavation until this minimum is attained.

It is particularly important with natural stonework to ensure that the finished level of the foundations is *well* below ground level to enable the stonework to be built in a normal manner (*see* Chapter 6) up to the damp proof course (DPC) level. Thus the foundations should be levelled off *at least* 150mm (6in) below ground level, and preferably deeper.

With stepped trenches two pegs are driven in adjacent to each other at each step, one peg for the lower level and another exactly one block higher for the upper level. Further pegs are levelled off at the new height from the second peg with straight edge and spirit level as before (Fig 24b) and their heights again checked to ensure the required minimum concrete thickness.

Work must now cease until the trenches, complete with levelling pegs, have been inspected and approved by the local building inspector.

Concreting in the Foundations

If progress is delayed by waiting for the building inspector then the trenches for the drains may be dug. However, once the foundation excavations have been passed you should not delay in concreting them in to the pegged levels.

Hand mixing of concrete for foundations and indeed of the mortar later required for the actual building work is arduous and an unnecessary waste of time for a large project such as this. It is far better to either hire or purchase a cement mixer. Considering the length of time the building work is going to take for this type of project, buying a mixer could prove much cheaper in the long run, especially if you can get hold of a secondhand one in good condition. You are not going into the construction business, however, so a large unwieldy and very expensive diesel or petrol powered model is unnecessary. Purchase a lightweight but sturdy electric mixer and avoid the problems of starting an engine in damp or cold weather, and running out of fuel.

Look after the mixer; always wash it out if it is to be left unused for more than an hour. The easiest way to do this is to scour it with a quantity of coarse gravel followed by clean water. Never hammer the drum to free accumulations of dried mortar. A bent drum will cause the mix to stick even more. If the mixer remains in good condition you will be able to sell it and recoup some of the cost when the work is completed.

The specification normally defines the mix for the foundations as 1 part of cement to 8 parts of 'all-in' aggregate; the aggregate is a ready-mixed combination of sand and particles of gravel of all sizes up to 40mm. This should be delivered to site and stored separately from the pure building sand which contains no large particles. Apart from water no further additives are required in the foundation concrete which should be made fairly wet (*see* Table 2, Appendix).

It is useful to have some assistance when concreting so that one person can man the mixer continuously whilst the other barrows the concrete into the trenches and levels it off to the pegs. Tipping should not be too close to the edge of the trench in case the sides collapse. If it is necessary to cross the trenches this should be done by means of short lengths of stout board resting on longer planks running alongside the trench edges to distribute the load. Where steps occur in the foundations, concreting should start at the lower level and with shuttering boards set up at the position of the step to hold the concrete in place at the new level. These are removed when the concrete has set. Protect the concrete from rain and frost until it has hardened.

To estimate the quantity of materials required it is necessary first to calculate the volume of finished concrete in the foundations from the plans. This is given by multiplying the total length of the foundations by the cross sectional area of the concrete (not the trench), the cross sectional area itself being the trench width multiplied by the required depth of concrete. The usual formula is:

width x depth x length = volume
(all measured in metres) (in cubic metres)

The amounts of cement and aggregate required can then be read off from Table 3 in the Appendix.

Drains

Organising drainage is one of those jobs that is carried out over a period of time. In certain circumstances some of the pipes to the drains might need to be laid under the floors so this work would have to begin directly after the foundations are completed. If such is the case it will be indicated on the plans. Also, there may be a long wait after the foundations are completed before the building inspector arrives and the go ahead to continue building is given. In the meantime there is nothing to stop you making a start on the drainage system. This is why drains are considered here, though in many cases work on the drains can be left until the house shell is completed.

If a perfectly adequate septic tank has already been installed there is no need for a replacement and the new system may be plumbed into this. But where a tank needs to be installed I recommend that the work is subcontracted since a mechanical digger will be required, not only to excavate the hole for the tank but also to manoeuvre the heavy concrete tank sections into place.

There is now an alternative to the heavy concrete tank. This is the flask-shaped glass fibre septic tank which can be bought from builders' merchants and manhandled into position. Though not heavy it still requires a very big hole to accommodate it. A word of warning about installing one of these tanks: immediately it is in position fill it with water from a hose to anchor it in place. Some builders using this type of tank for the first time have returned to site next day after rain to find the tank bobbing up and down in the flooded pit like a cork in a bucket of water!

With a septic tank it is normal to dispose of rainwater and waste household water separately. Rainwater from roofs is led through downpipes into soakaways, whereas household water from sinks, water closets, and baths is fed via soil pipes to the septic tank. This is in contrast to more modern households connected to the mains drainage where *all* excess water is fed into the central sewerage system. Where mains disposal is available, the owner is responsible for all costs involved in connecting his drains to this communal system. Where mains drainage is not available, a rates reduction is generally allowed, although the owner may have to pay to have his septic tank emptied from time to time.

If you inherit a septic tank that needs emptying more frequently than about twice a year, there is something wrong. It may be too small for your increased load, or there could be a blockage in the outflow into the subsoil. In such a situation it is best to contact the local council to avoid problems of pollution and possible disease.

Disposal of household waste water into a septic tank will be considered first and those linking up to a mains drainage system will need to follow the same basic procedure.

Wherever the pipes from the house to the septic tank meet or change direction a manhole is required. Their positions will be shown on the plans and must be strictly adhered to (Fig 9). To avoid interrupting the normal functioning of the household the existing drainage system remains operative at this stage. By installing all the external system now, interruption of this service is minimised when the changeover is made at a later stage of the project.

Excavation

Domestic manholes are generally 457mm x 618mm (18in x 24in) finished internal dimensions. To allow for the double thickness of brickwork and to facilitate laying the bricks, the excavation will have to be considerably larger. Since the new system is to be laid to a position determined by the existing drains, the first manhole dug is the one nearest the tank around the pipe at the position indicated on the plans. In other words start with the lowest manhole.

Care must be taken to ensure that the existing pipe is not fractured. It must be supported on bricks when the soil beneath it is removed. A bed of concrete approximately 150mm (6in) deep is laid in the bottom of the manhole so that the finished level just touches the bottom of the existing pipe. Before completing the manhole, the trenches for the soil pipes are excavated so that drain laying and manhole construction can be completed together. To be self-clearing, the drain pipes must be laid to an adequate fall and regulations set the minimum fall at 25mm per 10 pipe dimensions. Since domestic pipes are normally 100mm in diameter, this fall will be 25mm per metre run (1 in 40).

Using pegs and line, mark out the direct run of the drain from manhole to manhole on the soil surface as indicated on the plans, making the trench width approximately twice the diameter of the soil pipe. From the lower manhole excavate back roughly 3m of trench judging any fall by eye and starting with the bottom of the trench about 50mm below the concreted bottom of the manhole.

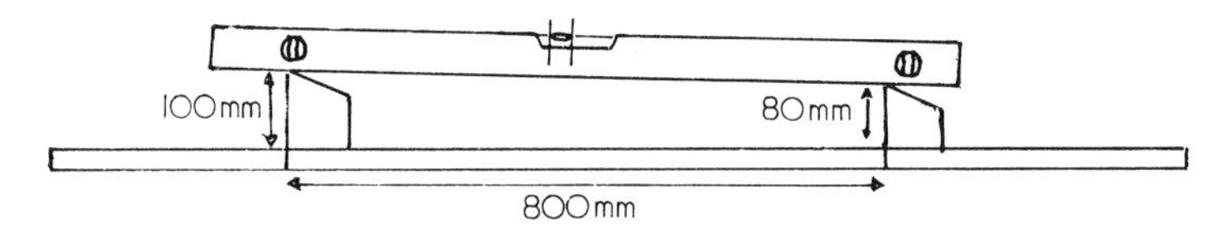

Fig 25 Readjusting the spirit level to provide an accurate guide for a constant fall of 1 in 40 for laying drains. (Distances in millimetres)

Before going further you must check that the minimum fall is being attained. Here is one method of doing this. Using the spirit level construct a true horizontal surface with blocks or bricks set about a metre apart and supporting a stout piece of planking. On this measure and mark an *exact* distance of 800mm between the supports. Next saw two blocks of wood, one *exactly* 20mm higher than the other on one edge, eg blocks 100mm and 80mm high on one edge, as in Fig 25, would be suitable. Place these blocks against the marks on the horizontal surface so that each block is to the same side of each mark, and are exactly 800mm apart. Lay the spirit level across the blocks and mark the new bubble position with adhesive plastic tape or, if the level is adjustable, re-align the bubble with the screws provided. When the bubble is exactly centred between the tape markers, a precise fall of 1 in 40 is given.

Using this modified level roughly check the fall in the base of the drainage trench and adjust your excavation accordingly, digging deeper or excavating less. If it is obvious, as on steeply sloping ground, that the excavation will be excessively deep by the time the next manhole is reached, adjust the bubble markers very slightly to steepen the gradient. Whatever gradient you use though, it should be constant for the whole length of the run. If it is certain that the trench is going to come to the surface before you reach the manhole then something serious has gone wrong. If the original drains worked to these falls then the new ones should. If you are working to a new septic tank and a totally new drainage system sue the architect and start again!

Laying the Pipes

Thanks to the new plastic and PVC materials, drain laying these days is child's play once the trenches have been cut and bottomed up to the correct falls. To achieve the perfect base to the trench and provide a solid support along the total length of the piping, the drainage trench is lined with a 50mm depth of coarse gravel or chippings graded out to a perfect fall from manhole base to manhole base. The pipe sections are laid onto this base and the joints made by simply snapping each new section into the collar of the one before according to the manufacturer's instructions, using a rubber ring to ensure a watertight joint. Because the collars are larger in diameter than the pipe these are bedded into the gravel. More gravel is added to firm the pipes in place but they should not be completely covered until tested.

At the manholes the pipes are passed through the brickwork and the brickwork built round them to ensure a watertight fit. The manholes are then bricked up to the required height to fit a standard inspection cover and frame which is bedded in cement mortar (Fig 26).

Building regulations require that the pipe joints are watertight and the local council will carry out their own tests on this (and check the effectiveness of the ventilation pipe) at a later stage. However, it is as well to test the drain pipes yourself before backfilling the trenches and this is best done on a dry day when the gravel around the pipes has a powdery appearance. To test the drains, close off the lower end of the pipe at the manhole and then, using a hose, fill the pipe with water from the higher manhole. Leakage of water from the system will show up after a while as damp patches in the gravel around the joints. Such faulty joints will have to be reassembled. Once you and the building inspector are satisfied that the joints are watertight the trenches can be backfilled and levelled off to the soil surface.

Finishing the Manholes

Within the manholes the water is carried between the inlet and outlet drain pipes by open channels which are cemented into place. These open channels are of standard shape to suit various purposes; for example a Y-shaped channel for directing water from two drains into a single drain run. When the open channel is in place, the floor of the manhole is *benched* to the channel, that is built up with mortar which slopes down from the sides of the manhole to the channel (Fig 26). If the manhole is sited in a driveway a heavy duty cover should be fitted to avoid the danger of fracture.

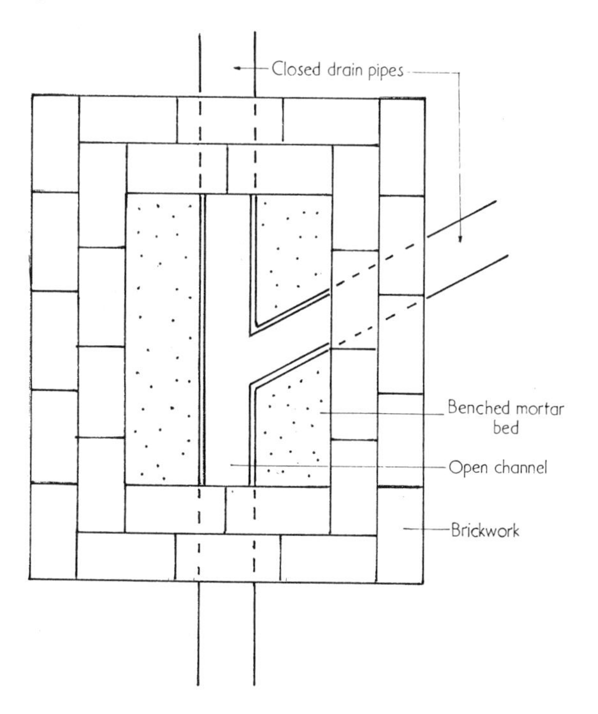

Fig 26 Construction of a manhole

The Ventilation Pipe

The ventilation pipe must be fitted to prevent gases building up within the drainage system. It is normal to use a single pipe which serves the double function of both a soil and vent pipe and this can be sited on any convenient wall of the house. It may be fitted internally or externally and its position will be indicated on the plans (Fig 9b). Household waste water from sinks, baths, showers and water closets is all directed to this pipe which then conveys it to the drainage system proper. It is important to remember to leave appropriate openings in the wall to carry the connecting pipework, rather than have to cut through stonework at a later stage.

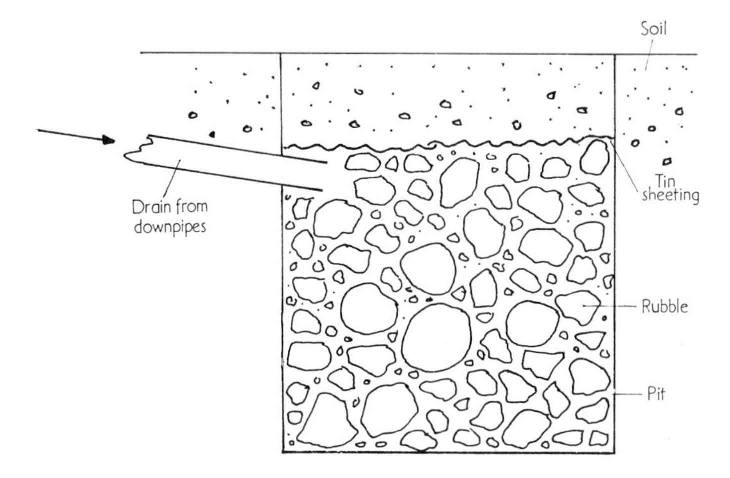

Fig 27 A typical soakaway for the disposal of rainwater

Disposal of Rainwater

To prevent overloading the septic tank the rainwater is disposed of in separate drains running into soakaways. A soakaway is simply a large deep hole sited well away from the building to prevent water seeping back into the foundations. The size of the hole required depends largely upon the free-draining nature of the underlying subsoil. Obviously, a soakaway on porous limestone need not be so large as one on heavy clay. On average, the dimensions will need to be of the order of 2m x 1½m x 1½m (6ft x 4ft x 4ft). This hole is two thirds filled with rubble and the drain pipe laid into this as close to the top as the fall from the house will allow. It is then covered with tin sheeting, or some other suitable material, before the hole is filled up with soil (Fig 27). The purpose of the sheeting is to prevent the soil from percolating into the rubble and clogging it up. The drain pipes are laid to falls as described for the household waste water and run in a direct line from the downpipes to the soak-aways. Connection to the downpipe is made with a curved section of drain (*see* Fig 68).

6

Work to Damp Proof Course

Block Walling

Building Regulations

The regulations for cavity walls require that they are of sufficient thickness to ensure stability, and the cavity should be a minimum of 50mm (2in) and a maximum of 75mm (3in) wide. The external walling must also resist the penetration of rain and snow, and all walling should be proofed against rising damp by the inclusion of a damp proof course (DPC) which must be at least 150mm (6in) above finished ground level. The cavity must also extend a minimum of 150mm (6in) below the DPC.

The two skins or leaves of the cavity wall must be properly bonded, and also tied together with wall ties of an approved standard and must be built of materials (blocks or bricks) which meet the necessary fire, strength and insulation requirements. To meet such basic thermal and moisture penetration requirements a solid wall would have to be at least 450mm (18in) thick. The standard cavity wall meets these requirements with an overall thickness of 250mm (10in).

Wall Structure

The basic type of external wall construction used for the proposed extension and illustrated in the plans might at first sight appear not only unusual but also unnecessarily expensive. It consists of a standard cavity wall built of two skins of lightweight insulating block to the outside of which is built 250mm (10in) (minimum) of stonework. The stonework is not simply cladded on as a thin skin, but is built as an integral supporting part of the overall walling and has many advantages over a simple decorative cladding. As well as providing good resistance to damp penetration, it gives the solid appearance of true stonework in keeping with the original. It also allows door and window frames to be set back so providing better weather protection for modern softwood frames, greatly increasing their life expectancy. The bulk of stonework further increases the weather proofing of the building, without the need for continuous maintenance after construction, and adds to the overall strength and stability of the structure.

You may wonder why the interior blockwork skins are necessary, but the construction of a cavity wall in random stone alone is very difficult and time consuming. Although requiring more materials this hybrid method of construction is far simpler. However, by far the greatest benefit is in the superior thermal insulation it provides over a standard cavity wall. In modern homes built with standard cavity walls, about 35 per cent of all heat loss occurs through the walls. Using the hybrid construction outlined in this book, heat loss through the walls is virtually eliminated. (If using coursed or partly dressed stone, the facework can be reduced in thickness to about 100mm (4in) but, if so, some of the advantages of protection and insulation are lost.)

Obviously the internal walls *need* not be built to the specification indicated here since basically they need to satisfy only the requirements of partition walls. However, the south wall (internal) of the extension (Fig 9a) has to support an external stone wall above the ground floor and *must* be built to these dimensions. Should stone be in short supply and the wall be destined for a plaster and paint (or wallpaper) finish inside, then 150mm (10in) hollow blockwork could be substituted for the stonework to the lean-to roof level. Personally, I would build the wall in the same manner as the external walls, allowing the choice of an internal stone wall in keeping with the existing frontage of the original house. Should this prove unsatisfactory it can always be plastered over at a later date, whereas a block wall cannot be transformed into a stone one. Internal stonework need not be 'cold' or drab. It can look most effective and has the added advantage of requiring neither maintenance nor decoration.

Marking out the Footings

The profile boards used for laying out the foundation trenches should have remained in place and be already marked with saw cuts setting out the internal and external faces of the walling. Lines can therefore be laid between the appropriate cuts immediately designating these wall faces. It is fairly simple to mark the *external* face of the second block skin once the line for the internal skin is in place.

Blocks are positioned inside and just touching the line as close to the

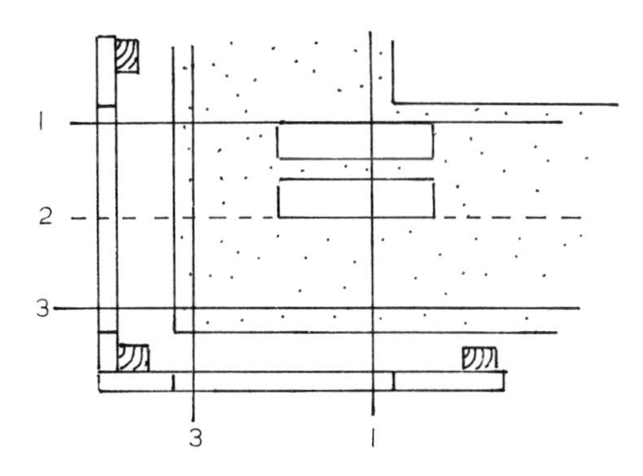

Fig 28 Marking out the various wall skins on the profile boards: (1) internal blockwork face; (2) external blockwork face; (3) stonework face. (Foundation concrete stippled)

profile boards as possible at each end of the foundations (Fig 28). Other blocks are then placed on the foundations opposite and inside these leaving a gap of about 60mm for the cavity. A line is stretched along the outside faces of these blocks over the profile boards which are marked and then cut. The blocks are then removed and the string stretched between the new notches on the profile boards.

Each profile board now carries three marker lines. The internal one marks the run of the *internal* face of the blockwork cavity wall. The middle line marks the position of the external face of the outer blockwork skin of the cavity wall, and the outermost line shows the run of the external stone facework. These lines should not be removed until the footing courses for all the wall skins are in place and set.

The Tools for the Job

The basic tools and equipment you will need are: a good quality builder's trowel, a spirit level at least a metre in length, a bricklayer's and a club hammer, a bolster and some chisels, a straight edge, some good quality line and line pins, a shovel for mixing, a mixer, a sturdy barrow and a number of clean spot boards positioned around the work at convenient intervals on which to place your mortar as required. In addition, since moving to Yorkshire, I have discovered another most useful little gadget used by bricklayers in this district. They call it a *line block* and make it themselves from a small piece of good quality hardwood. Fig 29 illustrates how to make your own although care must be taken to cut it *absolutely* square. If the idea catches on they may well become commercially available before long. It is even easier to align the quoins accurately in block and brick work using such a block than by using conventional line pins, as the block can be slid up and down the wall for use on each course. It has the added advantage that it does not leave holes in the mortar as line pins do which require pointing at a later stage. However, it may not give such accurate results on the outer stone face where the quoins used are not absolutely true.

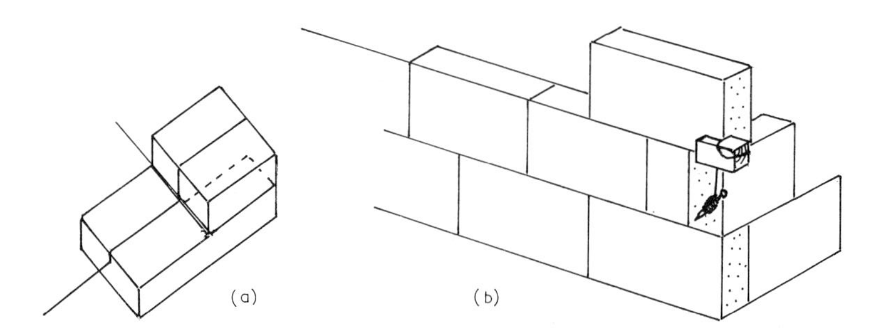

Fig 29 A line block: (a) detail of line block showing saw cuts and line; (b) the line block in use

Building the Blockwork Footings
It is essential that the footing courses (both block and stone) are exactly right, since the rest of the building is dependent upon the alignment of the courses below. Do not expect to be able to overcome inaccuracies later. Correct them immediately. If you are inexperienced you are going to find it difficult enough to keep the walling straight and square anyway. Do not attempt at first to complete vast yardages of walling at a single session; be content to work a long run laying a couple of courses only at a time until you gain in confidence and skill. Remember that blocks and even common bricks are not all perfectly proportioned and you are going to have to cope with slight size variations as well as keeping the block courses level, the walls upright and the returns square.

The mortar mix is of one part cement to three or four parts of sand (according to specification) plus an approved plasticiser (*see* Appendix, Table 2). It should be fairly wet to give a good bond although the use of a plasticiser reduces the amount of water required to make the mix workable. I strongly recommend the use of plasticisers in both blockwork and stonework since they make the mortar workable without being so wet as to dribble down the face. Furthermore, a dryish mix with plasticiser will become more malleable the longer it is turned in the mixer, within reason, hence better control of the mix is possible. But do not keep the mixer turning all morning as this is detrimental to mortar strength.

Always work from the inside of the building outwards, and finish by applying the stonework to the outer block skin. The first blocks laid will be those at the corners (quoins) of the internal block skin and the first course of blocks (the footings) will be built between these.

The importance of maintaining the foundations at a true finished level will now become obvious, for if these are level then blocks laid on the same thickness of mortar at each end of the foundations will also be level. Then it is simple to trowel out a bed of mortar on the corner of the foundations about 15mm thick and work the block into this to leave a finished joint of 12mm. The blocks should be positioned so that they are upright and just touch the strings from the profile boards, without causing any bellying in the string (Fig 30).

They should also run continuously around the construction so that all corners will be tied in throughout the whole of the building: in other words when looking up the corner of a wall the blocks are alternately end-on and face-on, and when looking along a single course the block at one end will be end-on and the block at the other face-on (although this is not so vital as the corner bonding).

Once the end blocks in a run are in position and have been checked for accuracy in both horizontal and vertical directions, the remainder of the blocks can be laid between them using the lines from the profile boards. Laying the blocks may at first prove more difficult than expected. The horizontal mortar joint for each course is easily regulated

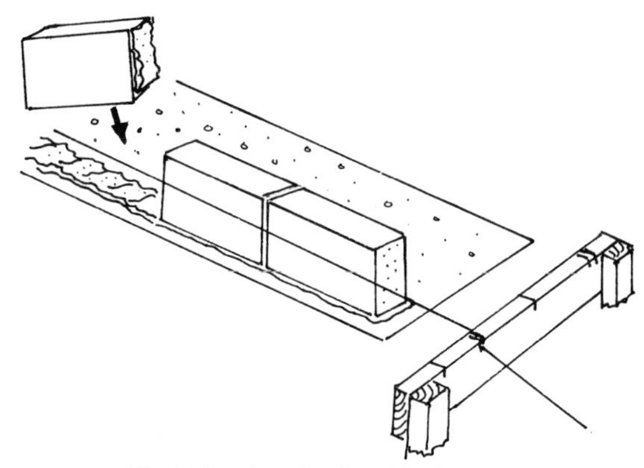

Fig 30 Laying the first block course

simply by trowelling the required amount of cement in an even layer onto the course below. However, the vertical joints always present the novice with problems. The temptation is to leave a small gap between each block and adjust the spacing by filling these in with mortar after all the blocks have been laid. But it is far better to persevere using the correct technique from the start and bond each block both horizontally and vertically as you go. To trowel in the open joints afterwards fails to provide a strong bond and takes an awful amount of time.

The mortar for the horizontal joints is laid onto the blockwork or foundation concrete below as already described, but the mortar for the vertical joints is laid onto the end face of the block to be placed in position (Fig 30). This is then rubbed down onto the block already sited to ensure a complete joint. The consistency of the mix is very important: too wet and it will run out of the joint, too dry and it will fall from the block before it is in position. If necessary, better adhesion can be obtained by first wetting the ends of the blocks before applying the mortar.

Clean the snubs of excess mortar off the *internal* face only as you proceed, to leave a smooth finish for the plasterer. Do not clean the cavity faces or the excess mortar will interfere with the cavity. There is obviously no need to clean the external skin as the stonework course will cover this. Cleaning block and brickwork is best done by simply rubbing the joints level with the block face once the cement has started to go off, but well before it is set hard. A stiff brush can be used to clean a large area quickly but be careful not to push the wall out of true. A finger is best for small areas. Do not use bare hands to rub the joints smooth but cut a finger out of an old pair of rubber gloves. In this way spaces, weaknesses and inaccuracies in the work are noted and can be corrected before it is too late.

Blocks rarely fit the space between the quoins exactly so some cutting will be necessary. It is not worth rushing out to hire or, even worse, buy a mechanical stone cutter. The blocks recommended here are particularly soft and easily cut by hand, but all types of blocks can be dealt with in the same manner. Use a club hammer and bolster to score a groove at least 6mm (¼in) deep around the block where the cut is to be made (Fig 31a). The unwanted end is then struck off with the hammer and, if necessary, the block 'trued up' with a bricklayer's hammer, always remembering to strike from the outside towards the centre (Fig 31b).

Once the internal blockwork footing skin has been built and checked, the outer blockwork skin is constructed by proceeding in a similar manner. Here the middle line from the profile boards provides the marker for the external face of the blockwork and a standard width of cavity of 60mm (2½in) should have been achieved between the two blockwork skins. The top of the footing course of the external skin is levelled off true with the internal skin. On no account should the external courses ever be higher than the internal; otherwise damp may penetrate to the interior via the wall ties which are put in position as the wall proceeds.

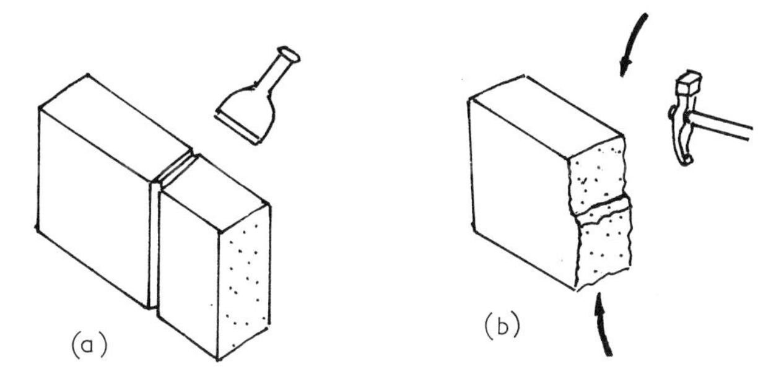

Fig 31 Cutting blocks: (a) scoring with bolster; (b) finishing with bricklayer's hammer

The level of the DPC is reached by building courses of common bricks or blocks onto each of the two skins of blockwork to the required height (a minimum of 150mm (6in) above ground level) and this should be done before any stonework is started. These are laid so that a brick or block always overlaps the vertical joint between two blocks below. The work is thus bonded with what is known as a *stretcher bond*. This is just as essential at the quoins as on the straight runs of blockwork (Fig 29).

Bricklaying using 'frogged' common bricks is considerably easier than aligning blocks. As before the end bricks at each corner are set in place and the line and line block positioned to mark the course. The rest of the bricks in the course are mortared into place by applying mortar to both the frogged face and an end face of each new brick to go in. These mortared faces are then worked onto the existing blockwork and the brick finally tamped firmly into place. Again the internal skin is built up first with spaces being left in appropriate positions to tie-in any blockwork partition walls (Fig 32). The second skin is then added and levelled off to this internal skin in the same manner.

The internal partition walls do not carry the weight of the roof and need be less massive in construction. However, since they are in contact with the ground in their foundations they must still include a DPC to prevent rising damp. Therefore these are also built before the concrete floors are in place out of a single skin of block tied into the main walls on alternate courses (Fig 32). Note, however, that a block or brick tie to these partition walls must not extend across the cavity of a cavity wall.

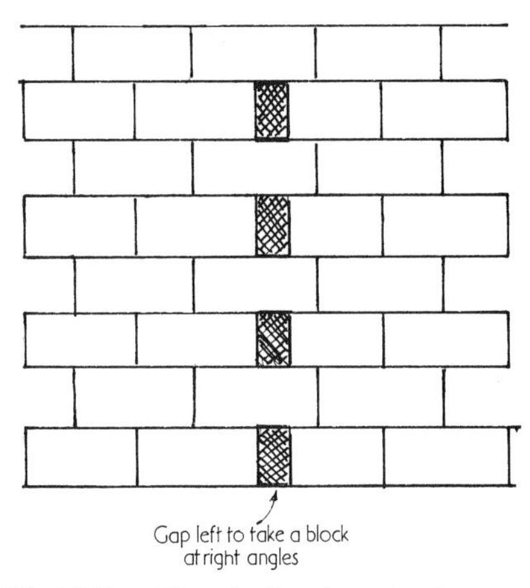

Fig 32 Providing facility for tying internal partition walls into exterior structural walls

In the example shown in the plans, the supporting eaves wall to the south which is part internal and part external must also be built with all its skins in place. However, since the work below the DPC is to be covered by the floor, there is no point in using stone below this level, so this can be constructed of blocks laid flat. Similarly, the footings are not carried across the opening of the kitchen to the dining area, so the concrete floor can run continuously through the two areas.

Where new or existing drains are intersected by walls, the walls must 'bridge' the pipes using steel or concrete lintels which will carry the weight of each leaf of wall and avoid pressure on the pipes.

When all the block and brickwork courses to the level of the DPC have been completed, work on the walling ceases until the concrete subfloors are in place. This is to allow easy access for excavation and barrowing in the concrete by not having to negotiate doorways.

Concrete Flooring

The ground floors must:

1 be strong enough to take the loads which may be imposed on them
2 prevent dampness rising from the ground
3 prevent vegetation growing into the building
4 provide a suitably hard-wearing surface

To satisfy these requirements solid floors are built in layers made up of a lower layer of hardcore, a fine layer of dust, a damp-proof membrane and a layer of concrete to which is later applied the type of finish required (Fig 33). Floor insulation can also be added which reduces heat loss by a further 10 to 15 per cent (*see* Chapter 9) and makes the floor feel less hard.

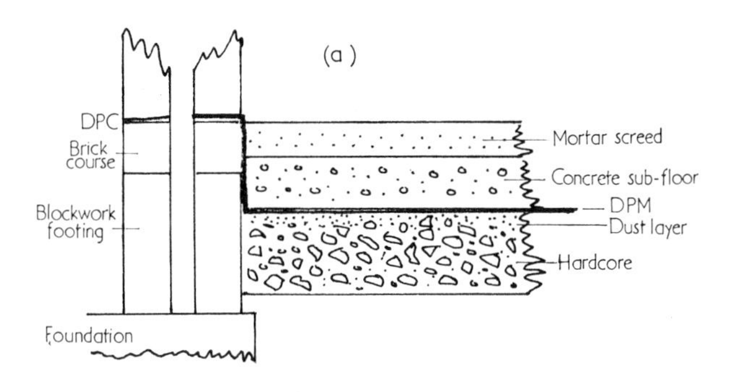

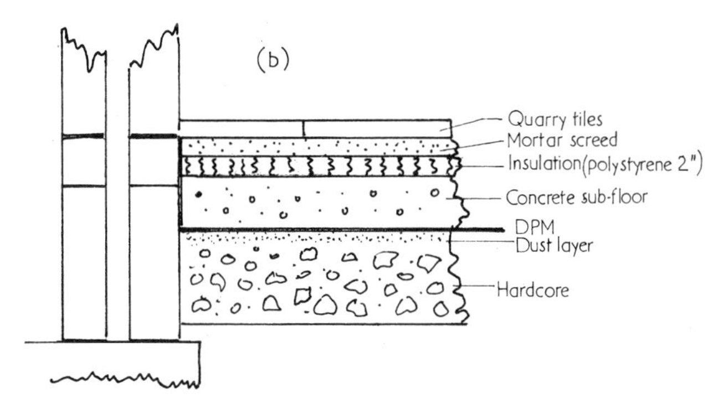

Fig 33 Solid floor sections: (a) without insulation; (b) incorporating polystyrene insulation and quarry tile finish. (Note that the stonework is not illustrated)

Excavation

Though some of the initial removal of vegetation and topsoil may have been done, the major excavation for the sub-floors is left until the level of the DPC is established, since this determines the finished level of the concrete floors. The concrete should be levelled off approximately 50mm (2in) below the DPC to allow the final floor surface to come level with the DPC, unless polystyrene insulation (usually 25mm (1in) thick) is going to be added in which case the concrete should be levelled off lower to accommodate this. The excavation, to accommodate 100mm (4in) of concrete and at least 150mm (6in) of hardcore, must be a minimum of 300mm (12in) below the DPC throughout the floor area — and another 25mm (1in) lower than this if insulation is going to be used.

A considerable amount of material is obviously going to have to be moved and barrowed clear from the area, even with a modest extension. (A room area of 3m x 4m (10ft x 14ft) could yield up to 15 tonnes of excavated soil.) So it is wise to organise the operation well beforehand. Decide where the excavated material is to go and how much room it will take up. Ensure there is good barrow access to the dumping site and start the excavation from the point furthest away from this site to avoid having to barrow from the bottom of the excavations over the top of the footings. Try to get some assistance so that there is a division of labour between digging out and barrowing.

Laying the Floors

The hardcore is laid throughout the excavation and well consolidated to give a finished level depth of 150mm (6in). The type of hardcore used depends on the materials available in different parts of the country. It could be obtained directly from a quarry as quarry waste or limestone hoggin, or as waste from heavy industry in the form of clinker or slag or even from building demolition in the form of brick, block, concrete and stone rubble.

If you've been lucky enough to obtain and demolish an old stone farm building, your hardcore should already be stacked in the form of small pieces of unusable building stone and rubble. But be sure not to include old pieces of timber or plaster in this hardcore since these will be affected by moisture and will break down in time to form hollow spaces. Since most types of hardcore is angular and could puncture the damp proof membrane (DPM), allowing water to penetrate, the DPM must be protected. This is done by covering the hardcore with a layer of fine material such as quarry dust or scalpings. When the DPM is in place but before the concrete is laid, the work must be passed by the building inspector.

The DPM is made of polythene sheeting of the required thickness which is obtainable from builders' merchants in rolls. Where overlapping of a sheet is necessary the overlap should be ample to prevent water penetration. (I always allow an overlap of at least 600mm (2ft).) Similarly, unless protected, water may seep through at the junction of the floors and walls. To prevent this the DPM is brought up over the footings of the internal block skin and the DPC overlaps this providing a continuous impervious sheet throughout the building.

The concrete mix is the same as that used for the strip foundations of the walls but, to cope with the volume of concrete required (see Appendix, Table 2), a mixer is essential unless a ready-mix is ordered and delivered to the site. Having your concrete delivered ready for use may sound the easy option but there are certain disadvantages associated with it, apart from the expense. You must have good firm access right up to the position where the concrete is to be spread and you require a great deal of fairly skilled labour to handle and spread the mix immediately it arrives. Drivers will not hang around while you move the concrete a barrowload at a time and by the end of the day you could end up with a mini-mountain of set concrete right where the kitchen floor should be!

When mixing and laying yourself, it is sensible to tackle and finish a single separate floor at a time, starting nearest to the mixing site. This means that once the concrete has set it provides a firm barrowing surface above the level of the DPM, and even barrowing over the wet concrete on boards if you go on to tackle another floor that day is better than risking damage to the membrane by barrowing over the DPM itself.

The concrete is roughly shovelled out to the required level and then tamped down to provide a rough tamped finish on which the final floor will be laid. The tamping is best done by two people using a tamping board. This is constructed as shown in Fig 34 and is far easier and less tiring to use than a simple length of timber held in the hands. Depressions will quickly show in the concrete by this method and should be filled and re-tamped as they appear.

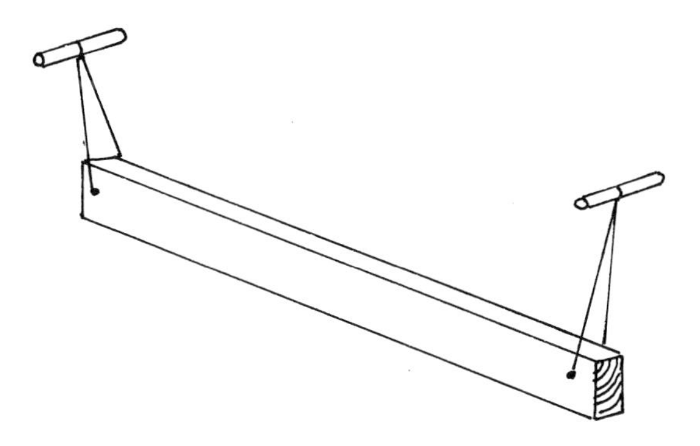

Fig 34 A simple two-man tamping board for compacting concrete

Note that if an internal soil and vent pipe is being incorporated then the outlet for this must be laid in place before the floor concrete is laid and the walls erected (*see* Chapter 5).

Once the floor concrete has set a course of bricks is knocked out at each of the door openings to allow a continuous run of finished flooring throughout and also to mark the door openings right from the beginning. It is surprisingly easy to forget a door opening when the walling work is going well at a later stage.

In certain circumstances, for example where the ground level falls sharply from the existing dwelling, a suspended ground floor is required. This is usually a wooden floor which is not directly in contact with the ground but spans the gap from one wall to another and overcomes the need for vast amounts of fill to raise the ground level. However, the construction of such floors is rather specialised and is adequately described elsewhere, eg in *Construction Technology*, Volume I by J. T. Grundy (*see* Bibliography).

Stone Walling

Little information is available on the use of random or natural stone in modern house building so the rest of this chapter and much of the next will be concerned with the techniques of working with natural unshaped stone. Such techniques are also explained in even more detail in *The DIY Guide to Natural Stonework*.

It may seem at first that there is little to choose between building in bricks, blocks or stone. They are all placed one on top of the other and require mortar to bond them. However, there are very fundamental differences indeed.

Blocks and (most) bricks have little if any intrinsic beauty in themselves. Each one is a replica of every other one, whereas each piece of natural stone has its own character and identity. Thus a block or brick wall is built solely for its structural properties and in many cases is rendered over so that the individual units cannot be seen. A stone wall, on the other hand, is built not only to satisfy structural requirements but also to be seen as a beautiful stone wall.

Bricks and blocks are always laid in horizontal courses with each unit being laid in exactly the same fashion as the one before. Natural stonework is not laid in horizontal courses and, since no one unit exactly resembles another, each piece of stone has to be fitted to the whole according to its shape. Some more regular types of stone may be coursed, such as millstone grit, but even so the courses are likely to be irregular in depth (known as *snecked coursing*) (Fig 2c). Ashlar work is always regularly coursed but in the extension described here coursed construction will be avoided.

In addition, blocks and bricks are bonded in a regular fashion, whether by using the standard stretcher bond or a more decorative array. This regular pattern of bonding, together with the coursing, emphasises the individual units in the wall. Although stone walls are bonded to improve stability such bonding is irregular. This, together with the absence of courses, means that the wall appears as a whole whether or not any marked patterning is used in the work (*see* Plate 15).

On any straight run of walling, as between returns, the bricklayer has only to concentrate on keeping the walling vertical and horizontal at each course to the finish. The stoneworker not only has to keep his walling vertical and lay the individual stones horizontally but must think ahead all the time. He must select stone according to size and shape and build up a memory of the stone shape and size available to him. He must build to the big stones and ensure the work is well tied in. He must start preparations for the finish well before the final stones are laid in place at the finished level. Apart from this the stonework has to be kept even

Plate 20 Generally poor stonework. Mainly mortar with separation of areas of small and large stone

throughout the wall face so that separate areas of large stones and small stones do not appear in the finished facework (Plate 20).

Both the objectives and approach to stonework differ from those working with brick and block. Patience and practice are needed to overcome initial frustrations, but most people are amazed how quickly they master this unfamiliar art. In any case, since only a single face of stonework against the outer block skin of the cavity wall is being considered here, some of the problems that have to be faced in the construction of free-standing stone walls do not arise.

Footings

The first run of stones laid directly onto the strip foundations are termed the *footings* and, even though most of the footings will be below finished ground level, the same amount of care should be taken over their construction as with the rest of the walling. The footing stones determine the accuracy of the wall and should not be scorned as 'dead work' that will never be seen.

The run of the faces is marked by the outer lines from the profile boards and the first stones laid are the quoins at the corners of the building. A single large quoin which (when bedded in mortar) exactly reaches the DPC level should be used (Fig 35a). Failing this, two or more quoins laid as shown in Fig 35b should be selected to attain the same finished level.

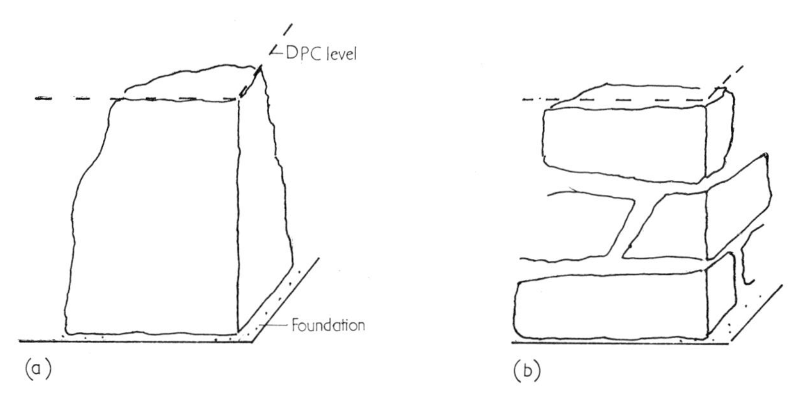

Fig 35 Setting quoins in the footings: (a) a single quoin stone to DPC level; (b) several narrower quoins built up to DPC level

Between the quoins large stones are bedded in mortar at intervals and wherever possible these should extend right up to the finished DPC level, except in any external doorway where they must finish some 75mm (3in) below to allow for a stone step. (This level should already be shown by the removal of the bricks from the internal wall skins at the door openings.) These uprights are set about 1m (3ft) apart with their outside faces barely touching the lines from the profile boards (Fig 36a). If the stone is slightly too deep its back should be crudely trimmed with the club hammer until it fits comfortably between the block skin and line (Fig 36a). On no account should it push out against the line however slightly since the line will no longer run true for its length and the whole wall face will be misshapen. The smaller building stone is bedded between these uprights (Fig 36b).

A dryish mix with plenty of plasticiser is used to bed the stones (*see* Appendix, Table 2) and to fill the joints between them which, unlike bricks and blocks, have to be done after the stone is in place. The spaces between the stones and blockwork are infilled with rubble and mortar to a level, then further small building stone is laid between the uprights until the level of the DPC is attained throughout the wall run (Fig 36c).

Building the stonework to DPC level only, to start with gives the beginner practice and builds confidence in a situation where the appearance of the wall is not vital so that attention can be concentrated on the accuracy of building. However, it is a good idea to consider the appearance of the work as you go along so as to begin forming ideas about using stone and to recognise mistakes to be avoided in future work.

Laying the Damp Proof Course

A variety of materials are available for the damp proof course, indeed in old buildings a line of slates performed this function, so what is obtained will generally be whatever is available at the local builders' merchant. Most common nowadays appears to be a PVC-type of material supplied in rolls of varying widths, the standard being 100mm (4in) for

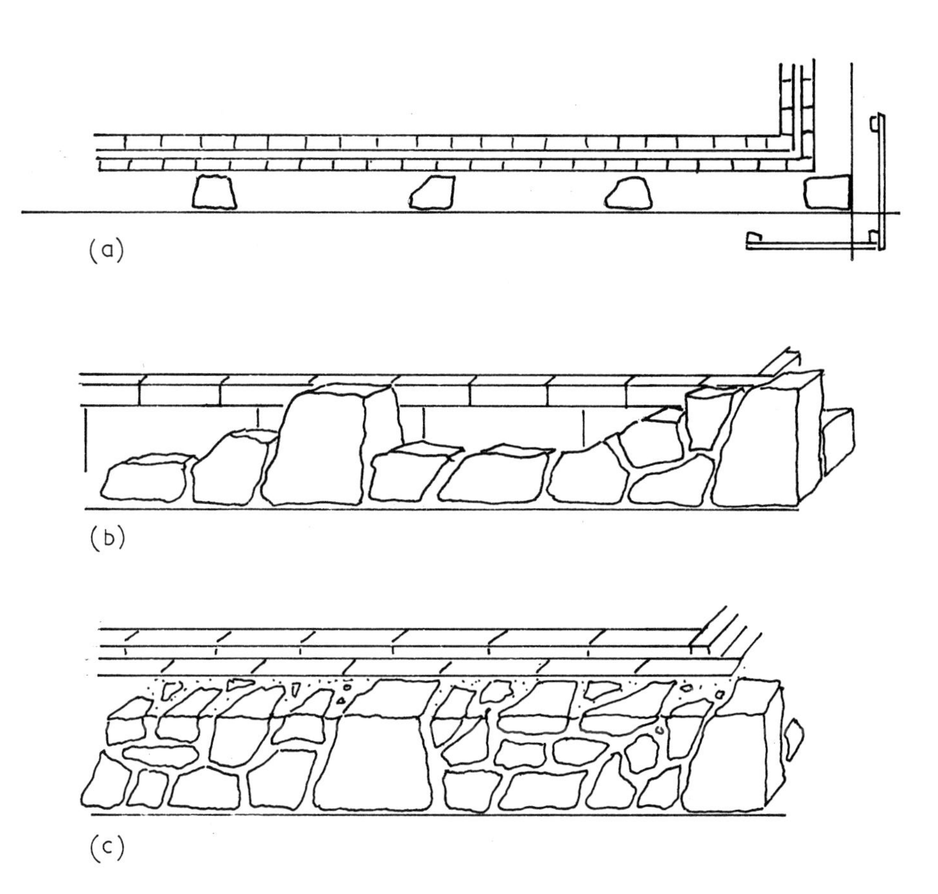

Fig 36 Building the stone footings to the level of the DPC: (a) placing the quoins and uprights — plan view; (b) building between the uprights — single block skin only shown; (c) finishing to level of DPC

the block or brick skins of cavity walls and this will suffice for the internal block skin. The total overall width of the outer wall skin (stone and blockwork), however, is much wider and requires a DPC 350mm (14in) wide. This may have to be ordered well in advance from the merchants or otherwise two, well-overlapped, widths of the more readily available 250mm (10in) wide DPC can be used.

The DPC is simply rolled out along the tops of the walls and held in place with a brick here and there. Any attempt to bed it down in mortar will prove futile. Where there is insufficient DPC material to complete a run it should be overlapped at least 100mm (4in) with a new piece. Similarly, the DPC should be cut to overlap on the corners of the walls. Under no circumstances should the DPC cross the cavity of a cavity wall and it must run continuously through the door openings dropping to the lower brick course under the doorway then rising again to the original level on the other side.

Before further building takes place the work has to be inspected by the local building inspector.

7

Walling to First Floor Joists

This chapter is entirely devoted to walling, including tackling ends and openings such as windows and doors. By the time the first floor level has been reached most of the walling problems will have been encountered and overcome.

General Blockwork

The internal skin of the cavity wall is built up to about four block courses then the outer skin is built up to this level and the procedure repeated again. The first course of blocks is laid directly onto the DPC and the second bonded over this in a normal stretcher bond. It is essential to ensure that the walls are perfectly vertical and the corners square at all times otherwise considerable problems may occur later when the roof is added.

Nothing should be leant against the blockwork until it is well set otherwise it may be pushed out of shape. Unfortunately attempts to push or knock it back into place only make things worse. If this happens the offending section must be taken down and rebuilt.

The two skins of a cavity wall are tied together with metal wall ties (Fig 37) to increase their stability. These are bedded across the cavity in

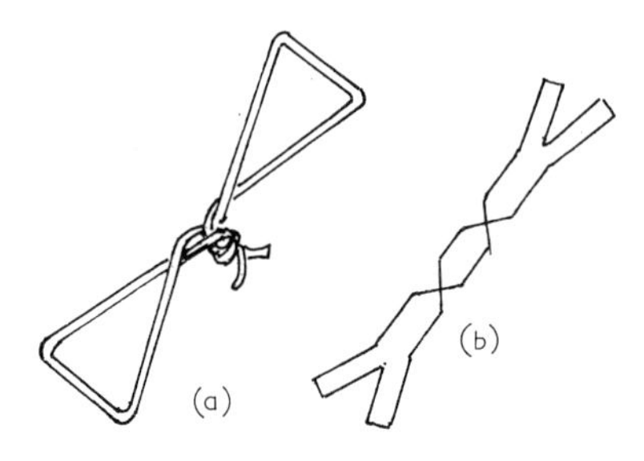

Fig 37 Common types of wall tie:
(a) twisted steel wire type with drip tie;
(b) twisted steel strip type

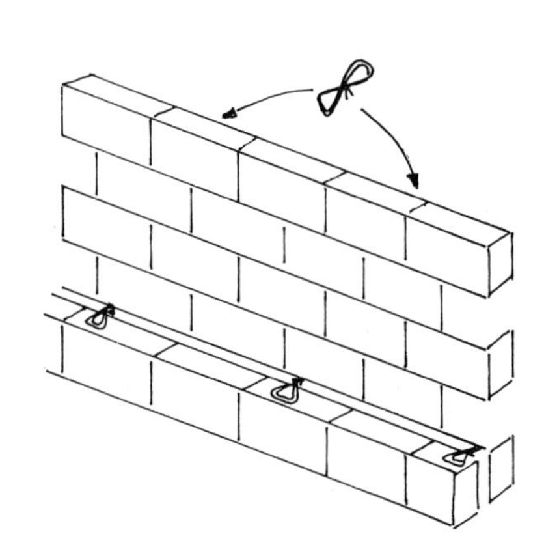

Fig 38 Placement of wall ties

the horizontal joints of each skin. Wall ties are obtainable from builders' merchants and should be kept clean. If crusted with cement they can transmit water across the cavity although this is unlikely in the present system of construction where the outer wall skin has a total thickness of 350mm (14in). The ties are bedded about a metre apart and staggered vertically (Fig 38). If using wire wall ties, the drip ties must point down.

If building four courses at a time I prefer to space the ties every four courses and build from tie to tie. If you are building only three courses at a time then space the ties every third course, this way the ties will not be forgotten. Ties may also be placed in the outer block skin to extend into the stonework at intervals and increase the bonding between block and stone. This, although recommended, is not essential if the stonework is well done.

If you are not confident about keeping the cavity clean of snubs of cement then pieces of 50mm (2in) batten or lath can be rested on the ties to catch the snubs. A staple and a length of string or wire at each end enables them to be pulled free of the cavity before each new set of ties is inserted (Fig 39).

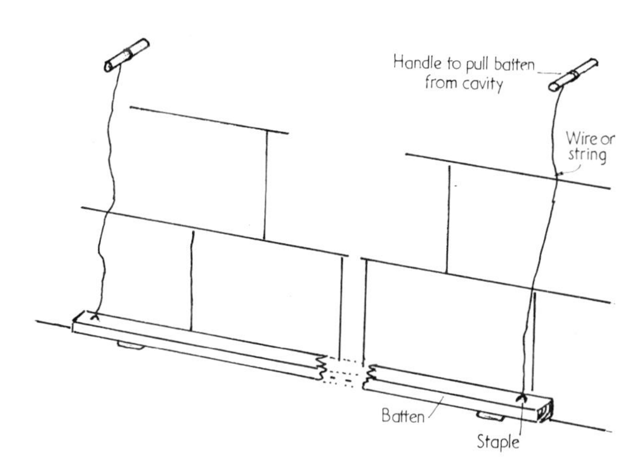

Fig 39 Keeping the cavity clean by means of a piece of batten (lath) resting on a run of wall ties within the cavity

Use the spirit level to check the horizontal level of the courses frequently and the vertical alignment of the corners, but do not leave it, or anything else for that matter, on top of one of the skins of a cavity wall. Many a valuable tool has disappeared forever into the bottom of the cavity!

From the start bear in mind the position of the bottom of the ground floor windows and calculate the number of courses required to the sills. This may not be an exact number of blocks and may have to be made up in common brick. This has one great advantage. Generally the sills of the ground floor windows will be at the same level above the DPC and a line of bricks in the blockwork immediately marks the sill position of the windows throughout the dwelling.

General Stonework

Build to Big Stones

Building to big stones is one of the main rules for working with random stone. It keeps the work even, sections the building work, produces a sound structure, avoids problems in stone selection and speeds progress. Large uprights have already been positioned in the footings and a further row are now positioned on the DPC above and between these. Use smaller mixed building stone to fill in the gaps between these uprights (Fig 40) to their approximate height but avoid a perfect level which would appear as a horizontal line throughout the finished facework.

Backfill with rubble, poor stone and mortar to make a *solid* wall to the blockwork. Then proceed to the next stage by placing a new series of uprights on the smaller stone below so that they are roughly between the previous set of uprights and directly above the ones below those (Fig

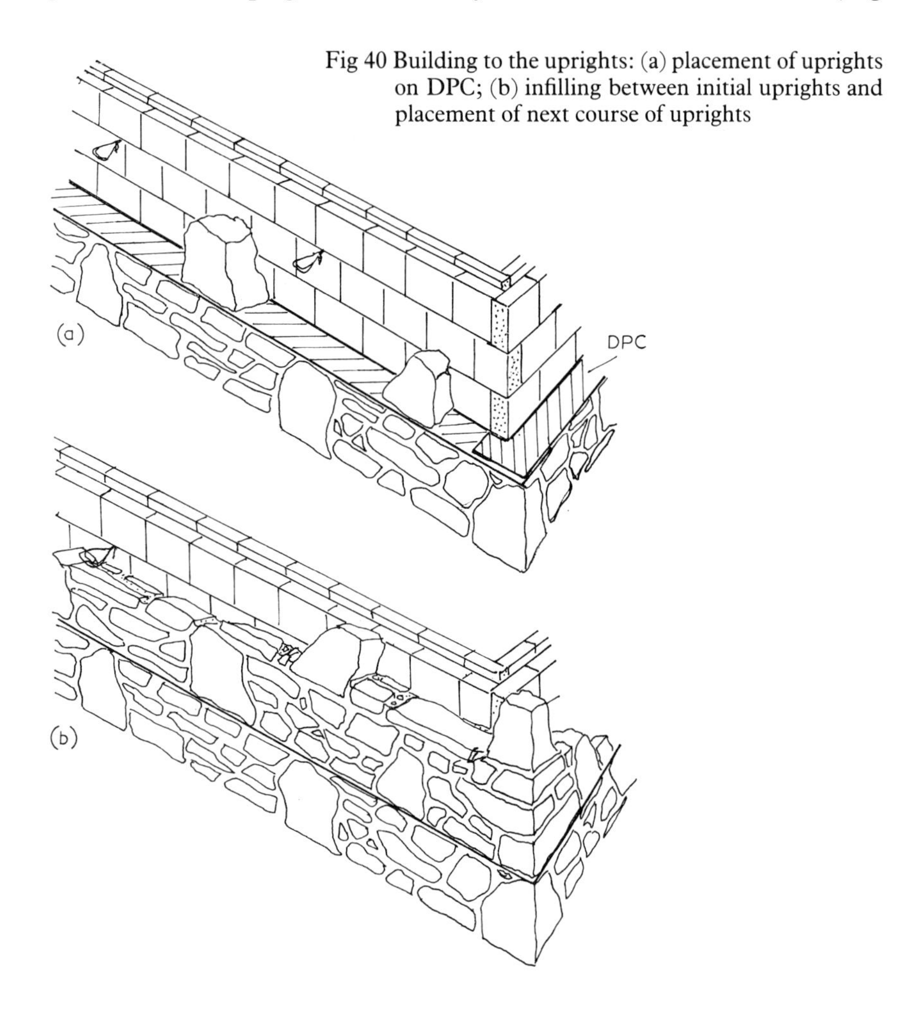

Fig 40 Building to the uprights: (a) placement of uprights on DPC; (b) infilling between initial uprights and placement of next course of uprights

40b). In this way the wall face grows in a series of false courses determined by the uprights. These large uprights need not be the same size all the time, in fact you would be lucky to find many of a similar size. However, they can be made random throughout the wall so as to retain the false course system.

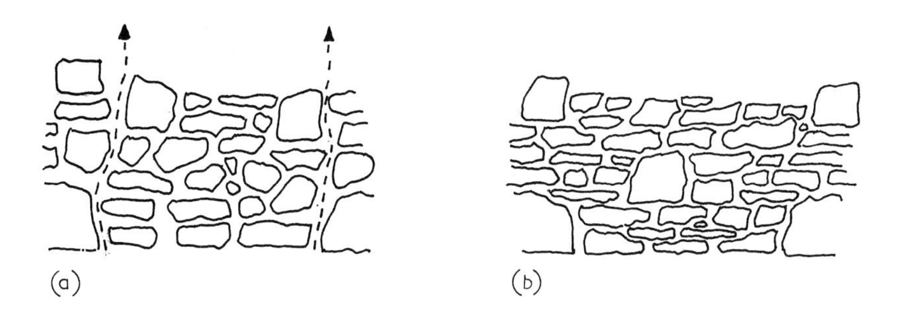

Fig 41 Bonding stonework: (a) incorrect — pronounced vertical rifts in facework indicated by broken lines; (b) correct — facework bonded so that vertical rifts are not produced; (c) tie-stones used in courses to bridge areas of small stone and produce a sound and boldly patterned stone facework

Bonded Construction

Just as brickwork and blockwork are bonded by placing the brick or block in the upper course over the joint between two in the course below, so too must every attempt be made to bond the joints in stonework. Wherever possible, one stone bridges the gap between two stones below and two stones above (Figs 40, 41b, 41c). This prevents the development of long continuous mortar joints (vertical rifts) running down the face (Fig 41a).

Such vertical rifts are a major source of weakness in stonework generally and any slight movement in the wall will immediately cause cracking along them. They are most likely to occur when building with a combination of very big and very small stone, rather than evenly graded material, and also where the uprights have not been carefully bonded over. For this reason a good supply of long flattish stone is very useful to tie across areas of uniform small stone (Fig 41c), and can be used to produce a patterned finish to the work.

Stone Shape

With fairly regular, squared stone it is simple to follow the two-over-one, one-over-two system of bonding. With random natural stone the problems are greater. Disregarding spherical stone which will not be used in the facework, your pile of building stone will be made up of three basic face shapes: flattish stones, triangular stone or a combination of each (Fig 42), although sizes may vary markedly.

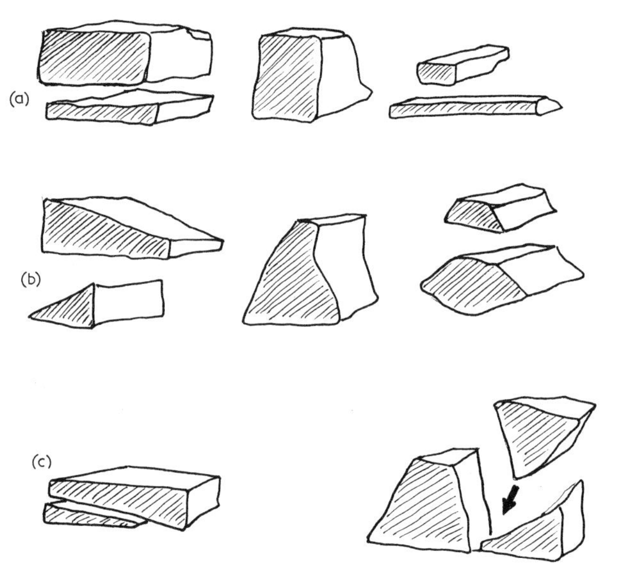

Fig 42 Basic stone shapes (faces shaded): (a) 'flat' stone; (b) 'triangular' stone; (c) use of 'triangular' stone as 'flats' or 'triangles'

One type of stone may predominate, perhaps flattish stone with some triangular and wedge-shaped stones. The stones would then be regarded as 'flats' and maintaining the overlapping bond described above with these is fairly simple. If triangular shapes predominate (including trapezium and diamond-shaped faces) the pile would be regarded as 'triangular' or 'mixed' and building would need to take account of this. To maintain the bonding, lay the lower stones so that the joint between them leaves an inverted triangular shape above, then invert a suitably sized stone into this space (Fig 42). You will very quickly become accustomed to making the spaces to accommodate the stone you have at hand, and will be on your way to becoming a true stoneworker.

Note, wedge-shaped stones may be used as either flat stone or triangular stone (Fig 42c).

Using the Mix

For people unused to building work, using a trowel efficiently and applying the mortar cleanly and evenly seems very hard to do. But it is vital to bed the stone well, seal the joints and keep the facework clean. These objectives are easier to achieve if the mix is just right. So keep it dryish but plastic with the liberal use of plasticiser.

Use a good sized builder's trowel, not a small pointing trowel. You may think you can manage this better, but it will slow you up in the end. It is far better to persevere and become accustomed to using the proper tool. You should not be tempted to use your hands: both the work and your hands will be the worse for it if you do. Use plenty of mix on the trowel and place it liberally onto the stonework so that you can work and tamp the next stone into it and pack the mortar well round each stone. Use the snubs that fall to the ground for backfilling and not in the facework since they invariably get coated in dirt and chippings which makes cleaning out the joints difficult.

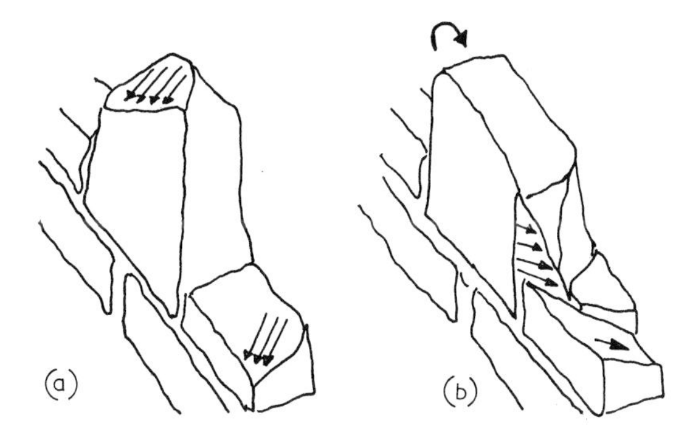

Fig 43 Stone orientation: (a) incorrect — top surfaces slope down and out; (b) turning the stones to gain greater stability

Orientating According to Shape

Owing to the infinite variety in random stone there may be many ways in which a single stone can be set in the wall to produce different outlines on the face. Several factors must be taken into account when orientating each stone. These may mean that the desired face shape cannot be achieved. Firstly, the individual stone's top surface when bedded in the wall must never slope downwards to the outside of the wall. The top should be level or slope inwards where it can be built up to a level to provide a stable horizontal platform for the next stone (Fig 43). If you do not do this gravity will tend to pull the following stone down the slope and there is nothing but the mix to prevent it slipping out of the wall. Test the stones before mortaring them in place. They should sit in a stable position without mortar. Do not prop them in with bits of board in the hope that they will remain there when the mortar hardens. When using long thinnish stones ensure that these are aligned in a true horizontal position, never slope them as this will mar the facework (Fig 44).

In attempting to overcome these problems the beginner is often

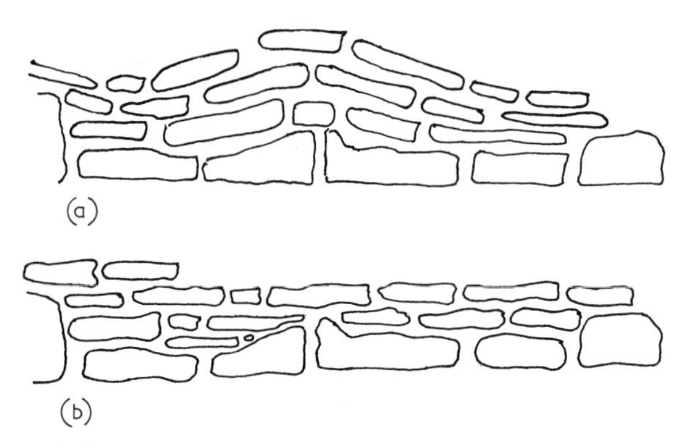

Fig 44 Horizontal alignment of thinnish stone: (a) incorrect — stones sloping and producing a 'wave effect' in the appearance of the wall; (b) correct — stones kept horizontal

tempted to build with progressively narrower stones so that they rest firmly on the broader ones below. This produces an ever increasing gap between the blockwork and stone facework and an inherent weakness throughout the wall. Simply filling this with rubble and mortar will not bind the wall; it is simply packing, and the weight of filling will tend to push the face outwards (Fig 45a). The development of a gap of this type should be prevented by building the facework and the backfill in a solid manner right up to the blockwork at all times (Fig 45b).

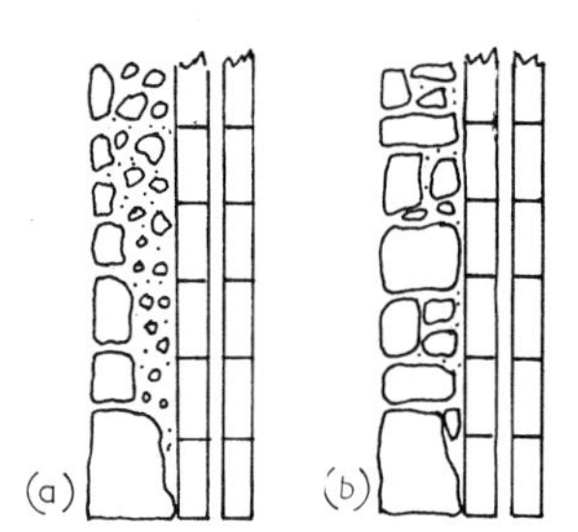

Fig 45 Walling sections illustrating a common beginner's fault: (a) weakness produced by building with progressively narrower stone and increasing amounts of rubble backfill; (b) correct building — stone facework solid to blockwork throughout

Chinking

Often a stone with a good vertical face may have a sloping base, yet it is desirable to use the vertical face in the wall. Chinking is a device for levelling up and supporting sloping stones by inserting stone slips and wedges between them. The terminology is from dry stone walling where other words such as *snecking* and *slipping* are also used to mean the same thing (Fig 46).

Where such slopes are slight the mortar itself performs this function, but with greater slopes a stronger, more lasting result is achieved if the gaps are both chinked and mortared. Chinking should be employed rarely and, if the rules of sound stonework practice have been followed, should be required only on the inside of the wall as part of the process of infilling.

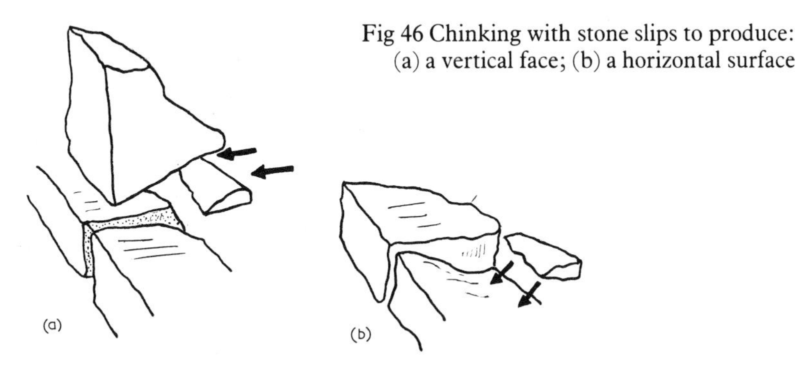

Fig 46 Chinking with stone slips to produce: (a) a vertical face; (b) a horizontal surface

Finishing to a Level

With a wall of any height, you must start to think about the finish and prepare for it long before you get there. In a house, such finished levels arise wherever there is to be an opening along the run of the wall, for example to accommodate windows. If a sill is to be incorporated then an allowance for this must be made when calculating the finished level of the stonework below the frame (*see* Fig 57b). So it is important to ensure that the last run of uprights finishes preferably at, or failing this, below, the final required height.

To do this it is easiest to mortar in the two uprights at the ends of the wall run so that their tops are at the exact finished level required. Then run a line centred between them (Fig 47a). On long runs an intermediate upright may be necessary to prevent the line from sagging. The

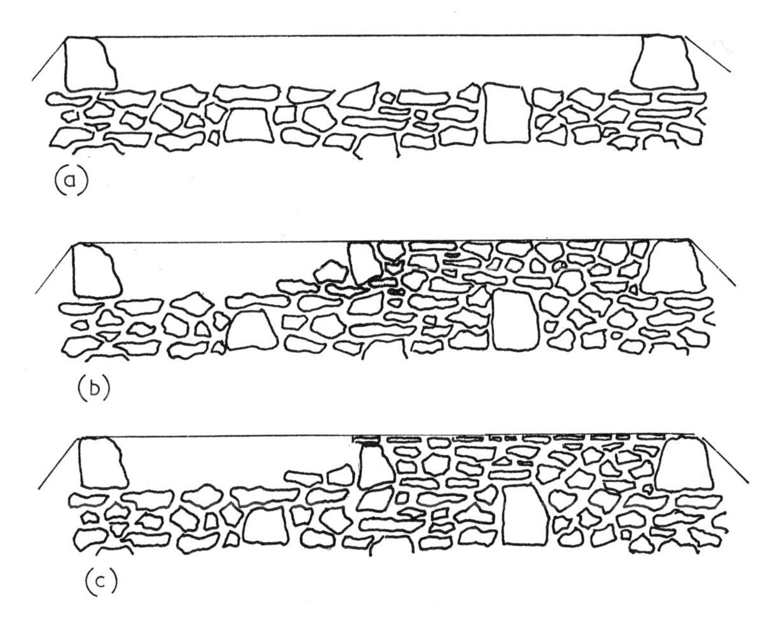

Fig 47 Topping off the wall: (a) setting the finished level with large uprights; (b) finishing correctly avoiding a final course of thin stones; (c) finishing incorrectly by using a final course of small thin stone to reach the level

tightened line will now represent the final finished level of the wall run and can be checked with straight edge and spirit level if required. If true, *topping off* can proceed along the run to the line.

First, set the uprights in place so that they reach the line wherever possible, or finish well below the line if not. If just slightly low they should be raised to the required level on a bed of thin stone rather than using the thin stone later on top to make up the difference. If a good gap is left between the uprights and string they can be safely bedded and the stonework brought to the level of the line by building over them in the normal way. Small thin stones should not be used as a topping off layer to bring a wall to its required level (Fig 47c).

As before, the stonework is built up between the uprights to the required level, working to a big stone as usual and making certain that as a general rule a line of thin stone is never employed as the final course. Such thin stone should always be placed below heavier stone, not above it (Fig 47b).

Turning Through an Angle (Returns)

A wall must stop somewhere, be it at an opening for a door or window, or the corner of the building. In practice the wall does not 'stop', it changes direction. Such changes of angle in the facework are loosely termed *returns* and generally involve turning the facework through an angle of 90° (right angle). Regardless of whether one is constructing a doorway, pillar, gateway or corner, the basic techniques remain the same. Only the selection of stone size might differ.

The basic building unit for turning through a right angle is the quoin stone and a selection of possible quoins from a pile of random stone is illustrated in Fig 14. These should have been stacked in a separate pile from the outset so that they are accessible as needed. It is the faces which are at right-angles to each other on the individual quoins which make up the right-angled return of the total construction. This is the only way returns can be made, so quoins are far too valuable to be squandered in the main facework. However, if true quoins are in short supply, very attractive and natural looking returns can be produced from a few well placed perfect quoins interspersed with other less perfect ones (*see* Plate 15).

Not only must the corner be kept upright but also the stones forming the return must tie back into each returned face of the wall alternately. This probably sounds very complicated but is more easily demonstrated in Fig 48. Tie-stones on returns are most important since the returns, and particularly the corners of buildings, are subjected to the greatest stresses. In choosing quoins avoid selecting those of the same size and thickness: make them random as with the walling stone itself and be sure to include long thin stones which will tie back into the wall faces at regular intervals. If the quoin stones are not tied-in to the body of the wall they will certainly break away in time (Fig 49).

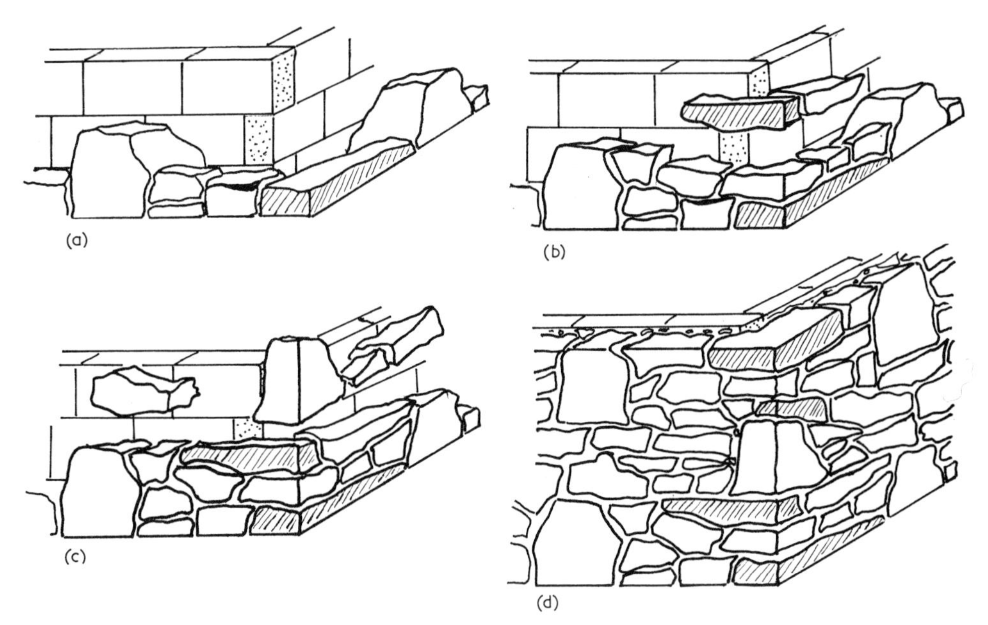

Fig 48 Stages in turning the wall through a right angle using rough quoins. (Tie stones shaded and only a single block skin is illustrated)

Fig 49 A weak return: (a) even stone selected for quoins which are not tied into the rest of the facework; (b) cracking and collapse as a result

Keeping the Walls Vertical

The walling is kept vertical by working from a line set between two vertical returns, therefore it is essential that the returns are built perfectly. Unfortunately maintaining a square upright return generally poses problems for the beginner and failing to get this exactly right means that the rest of the walling gets out of true. As far as stonework is concerned there is no substitute for the critical human eye together with the patient determination of the human will.

The quoin stones on the return must be set accurately and individually from the start using whatever technique you find most suited to you. Since you are working from the ground upwards, no plumb-line can be hung from the sky to provide a perfect line for the corner. A simple guide can be produced by bedding two scaffolding poles at each face run, approximately 300mm (12in) out from each corner of the building. These must be bedded into the ground to ensure that they are stable and vertical. Building lines crossing from these will mark the corner and returns. They can be moved up the poles as the walling progresses. It is important to check constantly that these guides remain vertical, particularly when the stonework gets higher and the line tends to pull the poles inwards.

Personally, I find this method unsatisfactory. I prefer to build by eye, checking often with the spirit level. The ability to work this way comes with experience and confidence and one must be able to stand well back to judge the construction critically as it progresses. But beware when working on scaffolding!

Once the quoins are perfectly in position on the returns then a line strung across their faces will mark the run of the face for the uprights in any length of wall run. When building the stone facework for the windows or doorways, it is important to remember to run the line right across the opening to keep the opening true with respect to the overall wall face. If the line is taken only from the window return to the building corner, there is nothing to act as a check that the opening does not bulge or become indented with respect to the wall as a whole.

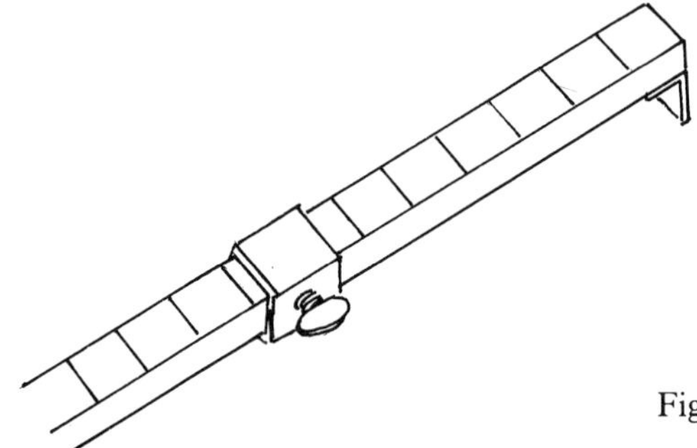

Fig 50 A simple slide marker for checking fixed dimensions

An additional check, apart from the line, can be provided by a marked piece of painted batten (lath) about a metre in length. It is particularly useful as a back-up when building stonework against a block wall *in situ*, but can be useful for checking other dimensions as well. This *slide marker* is illustrated in Fig 50. When the line is in position from the quoins at each end of the wall run, the line should be a constant distance from the external face of the external block wall. The slide on the marker is set to this distance and the line checked throughout its length for any deviation. If the distance of the line from the block wall varies to any marked degree then the setting of the quoins and the blockwork must be checked again.

Special Angles

Occasionally the stonework must be returned through angles which are not right angles: perhaps for flared window returns which allow more

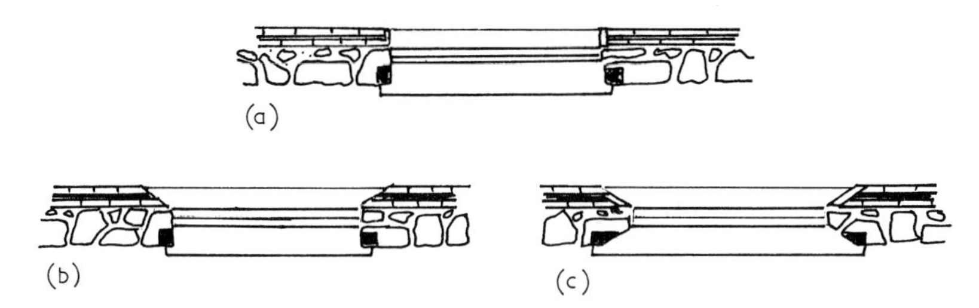

Fig 51 Plan views of window returns: (a) all returns at right angles to face; (b) external return at right angles, internal flared; (c) all returns flared

light through small windows into a room. Various types of window return are illustrated in Fig 51. Such special angles pose greater difficulties than the conventional 90° return, since the right angle is instantly recognisable as being exact or not, whereas I defy anybody to draw straight off an exact obtuse angle of, say, 120° without reference to either a protractor or right angle. The most common special angle used for window returns is the obtuse angle of 135° (which is 1½ right angles) and, since windows are such focal points, the stones making up such returns must be cut accurately. It is not coincidence that many buildings with otherwise roughly dressed stone have the window surrounds built from single pieces of stone sawn to the desired angle.

When using random stone it is best to make a simple template out of pieces of batten to reproduce the angle required and sort through the stone selecting those pieces which approximate to this template (Fig 52a). These may then be stored separately, like normal quoin stone, until needed. Two pieces of stone may be used to form the angle (Fig 52c) but this should only be used occasionally in the return otherwise the outline becomes softened and distorted in appearance.

Softish stone which is not too bulky may be cut either by hand or with a machine to produce the exact angle required for the return.

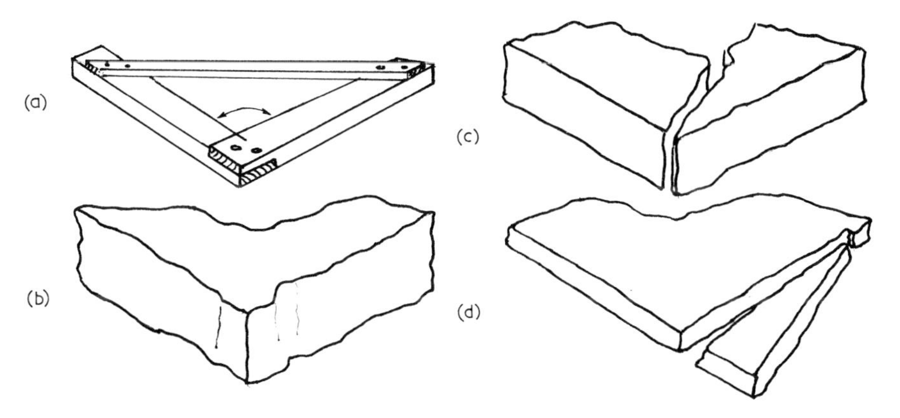

Fig 52 Obtaining stone for special angles: (a) template; (b) stone with approximate angle; (c) using two stones to form the angle; (d) cutting thinnish stone to form the angle

Working and Shaping Stone

The techniques of working and shaping stone cannot be taught by words alone and only come with practice and apprenticeship. However, when working with stone it is often necessary to undertake rudimentary tasks in shaping and cleaning that are well within the capabilities of the average handyman.

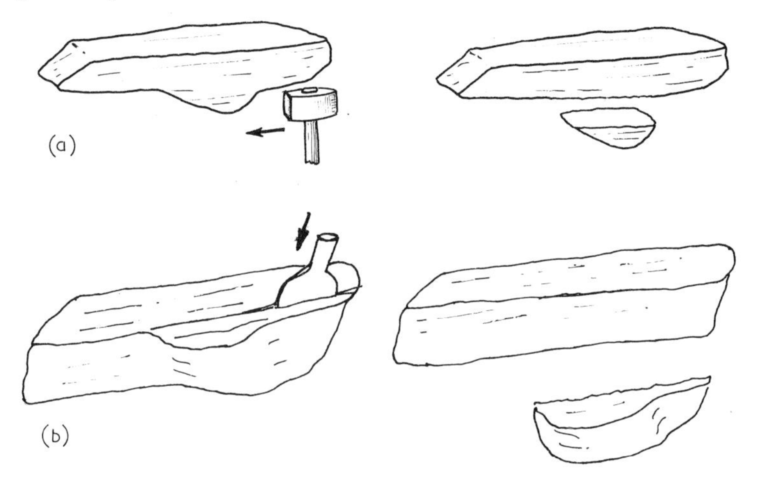

Fig 53 Removing protuberances: (a) striking off with a hammer; (b) splitting off with a bolster

Occasionally a projection or lump will prevent a stone from being seated firmly in the wall. While this might be overcome by chinking, it is better to remove the projection itself. This can be done by striking sharply with the club hammer against the steepest side of the lump in the direction of the grain (Fig 53), if necessary cleaning up with the bolster. Should this hammering action simply powder the stone then the protuberance should be removed by splitting the stone along the grain with hammer, chisels and bolster (Fig 53b). If such irregularities occur on the face of the stone they should be removed by striking from the outside towards the centre of the face and not vice versa. Always clean and shape the stone before it is bedded in the wall. Attempts to hammer off lumps later can dislodge the stones and damage the wall.

With random stone, and particularly in the case of the uprights, the desired face may not form a perfect right angle with the plane of bedding in the wall (Fig 54). If the departure from the vertical is very slight the stone face need not be shaped, *providing* you bed the stone with its *upper edge* at the true aligned position. This will mean either overlapping or setting back the *bottom* of the stone. I have often been asked why the upper edge of the stone face must be aligned rather than centring the stone or compromising in some other way. The reason has nothing to do with aesthetics. It is simply a safeguard against getting out of true when building considerable areas of stonework. By the time you return to that area of facework again, any peculiarities in individual stones are likely to have been forgotten. So, as the stones above are aligned to the top edges of the stones beneath, it is important that all these should be exactly right.

Where curvature of the face is pronounced, it must be trimmed to allow reasonable alignment. This is done by nibbling away the protruding edges with the hammer until a reasonable face is produced with clear horizontal edges for positioning the stone.

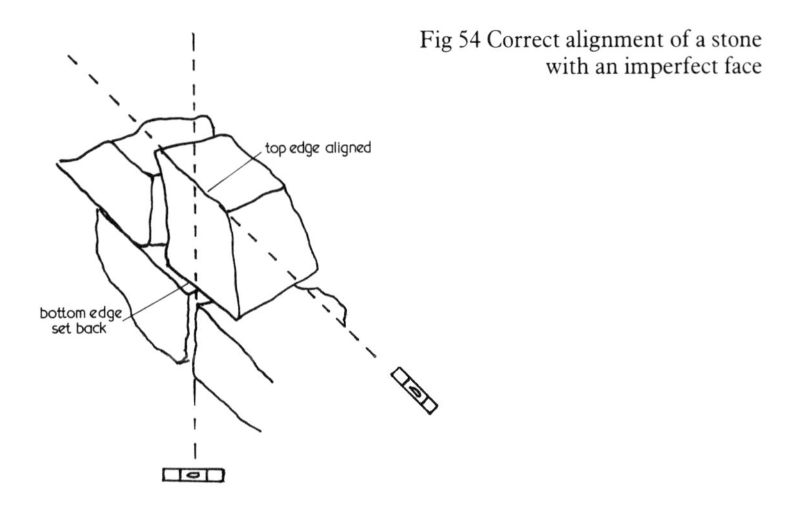

Fig 54 Correct alignment of a stone with an imperfect face

Making Quoins

Even if you have separated out all stones suitable as quoins and resisted all temptations to use any of these in the main run of the wall, very often there are still insufficient to complete the job. At some stage it may be necessary to shape quoins cut from other stone. This should be done whenever a suitable stone comes to hand, rather than using all the best quoins at the bottom of the walls and ending up with poorly defined corners at the top.

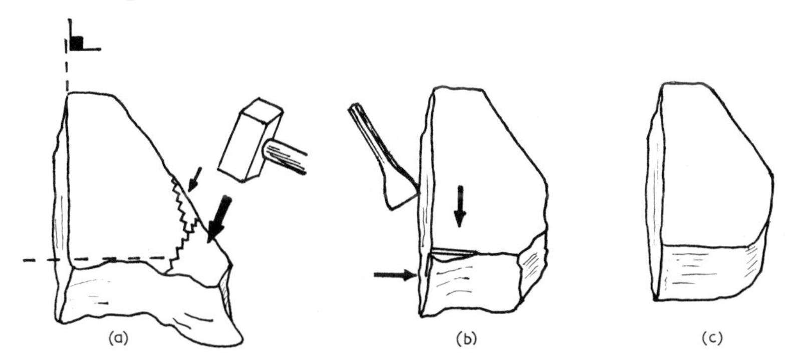

Fig 55 Stages in shaping a quoin stone

To cut quoins you require a lump hammer, a mason's or pitching chisel and plenty of patience. Start off with thinnish regular stone and work up to the bigger chunks. It is also best to begin with pieces that are almost right-angles and get the feel of the work by improving these. Break off excessive waste lumps directly with the hammer, then fine up to a previously scored mark with the chisel, cutting away a little at a time (Fig 55). Always work the stone from the outside to the centre angling the chisel slightly into the body of the stone. Do not try to cut very hard stone at the beginning; use the softer limestones and sandstones. Nothing encourages effort like success, but do not be upset by the odd failure. Look on the bright side: you may have failed to turn the stone into the ideal quoin, but it could now be the exact piece you need for some other place in the wall!

Pointing

This is the term given to the process of finishing the joints in either brickwork or stonework. Although its description has been left to the end of this section, attention to the joints must continue right through building before the mortar sets.

Joint finishes can be divided into two main categories: *raised* or *recessed* (Plates 21 and 22). Some general considerations are pertinent to both and will be discussed first. The pointing should enhance the stonework not obscure it. Personally I consider this to be its primary function. A wall without attention to the joints is a mark of either

(Left) Plate 21 Raised pointing. *(Right)* Plate 22 Raked out pointing creating shadows which emphasise the stonework

Plate 23 A thoroughly bad piece of workmanship on all counts!

laziness or inexperience and in both cases more often than not accompanies poor building work in general (Plate 23). However, pointing has a practical function too. Working the mortar into the joint smoothes its surface making it less permeable to water.

Whatever style is adopted, the stone surface must be cleaned and the joints attended to before the mortar has set. Using a dryish mix with plenty of plasticiser, the mix generally hardens enough to give a good finish to the work about an hour or so after the stones have been laid, and remains workable for about four hours. Therefore it is ideal to point up the work at the end of each building session.

Recessed Pointing

The beauty of stonework, particularly random stonework, is in the stone and in the way in which it is laid. The jointwork should enhance, not mask this. (Compare Plates 21 and 22.) The way to make pointing highlight the work is either to rake out or cut back the joints. This creates shadows which emphasise the stone shapes. The surplus snubs and smudges are cleaned from the face of the stone, and the top centimetre of mix in the joints either completely scraped away to leave a hollow effect (Fig 56) or cut back to leave a central ridge through the joint exactly following the line of the stone. This can be done with an old kitchen knife although I find a worn putty knife best.

The major criticism of recessed pointing is that it permits water to lodge in the joints increasing the risk of it penetrating the building. While this may be important in single skin brick or block walls, it is hardly likely to occur in the massive construction adopted in our example. However, the chance of frost damage could be increased.

Raised Pointing

This includes all types of pointing which are not recessed, including flush pointing. In some cases workers may brush off the joints before the mortar has set to give an overall smooth appearance with the joints flush to the stone surface. This reduces shadows and disguises the stone outline. Its only merit is speed (*see* Plate 20).

Raised pointings are laid on to stonework after all building has been completed and generally overlay smoothed out joints (Plate 24). Various styles are adopted, from those which faithfully follow the joints to the wiggly lines called *snail-creep* that wander over the face in a manner bearing no relation to the actual stonework (Fig 56d). Their only excuse can be to cover up poor workmanship beneath. In fact they often emphasise it.

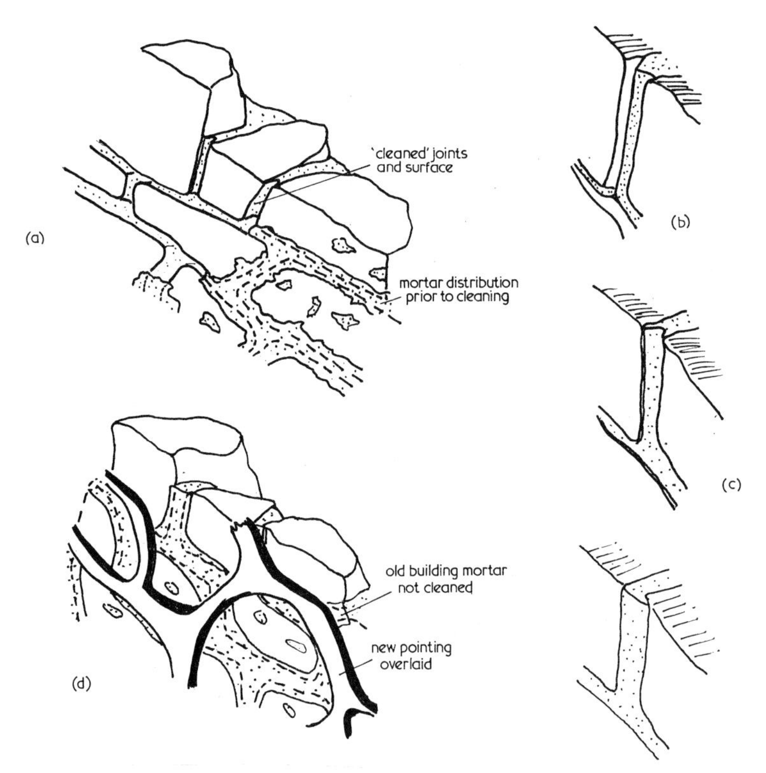

Fig 56 Pointing: (a) cleaning up the joints; (b) ridged cut back pointing; (c) raked out joints; (d) snail creep raised pointing; (e) flush pointed joints

Plate 24 Raised pointing masking the outlines of the stones

Doors and Windows

It is far and away the best policy to order window and door frames early and have them available on site when building begins. They can then be firmly and exactly built into the walling as it progresses, rather than leaving openings which may prove slightly inaccurate later. In this way the walling will be built to the frames. This should apply to both specially made and standard frames.

Building in the Frames

The techniques for dealing with both doors and windows are very similar and can be described together. Door frames are provided with struts across the corners and bottom to keep the frame square. On no account should these be removed until the frame is securely built into the wall. Window frames may or may not be strutted according to their type but, if they are, the same rule applies.

In a normal cavity wall construction the frames are situated on the external wall skin and the blockwork return is to the inside. In the method of construction being adopted for our extension, the frames for both doors and windows are built immediately to the outside of the external block skin, that is back in the stonework. This provides a deep sill both internally and externally, and provision must be made for the fitting of the solid stone sills at a later date.

At the door and window openings the level of the bottom of the frame is marked by the blockwork, which *must* be level. To accommodate the sills, or step, the stonework will have been levelled off at the required distance below this. So, to bring the frame up to its proper height, it is rested on two blocks of wood which are bedded level in sand (Fig 57). The frames are anchored into the wall by the horns and additional strength is given by screwing galvanised wall cramps to the jambs. These are better than nails or screws (Fig 57a).

The vertical and horizontal alignment of the frame is determined with a spirit level and the frame held firmly in position with a suitable board (Fig 57a). Since the cavity will be closed by the blockwork return, it must be protected from moisture penetration. In a standard wall this is done by running a strip of DPC down the return on the inside of the external skin. In the present construction a strip of DPC is run down the back of each jamb (Fig 57a).

The blockwork returns are built to the height of the frame first, making sure that the corners are bonded. Then the stonework return is completed to the same height and this will anchor the frame firmly in position (Fig 57b). The wooden blocks are left in place at this stage and will not be removed until the sills are ready to be slipped into place. Once the frames are built in position and the walling set the lintels may be added.

Lintels

Unless a frame actually reaches roof level, the wall must be continued over it. Frames are not designed to carry the weight of walling materials so the load must be borne by a lintel which comfortably spans the gap above the return. The overlap should be a minimum of 100mm (4in) either side. There are many forms of lintels to suit different purposes and different finishes.

For standard window and door openings, pre-cast concrete lintels are commonly used where the work is to be rendered or plastered over. This type of lintel would be used to span the return of the block walls (Fig 57b). Where the facework is exposed, as with facing brick or stone, such lintels would be ugly and a different type is required.

The lintels may be formed *in situ* out of concrete faced with stone, but it takes a long time for a lintel to set and strengthen and this delay can hold up the rest of the building work. *In situ* lintels are described in some detail in *The DIY Guide to Natural Stonework*.

Where facing brick or regular narrow sawn stone is used, special lintels which are manufactured out of steel carry the brickwork across the span without exposing the lintel. These *'catnic' lintels* can be purchased from builders' merchants but are not suitable for the present type of stonework where the depth of stone facework is too great. With 100 to 150mm (4 to 6in) facework catnic lintels are ideal since they are lightweight and easy to handle even in long lengths. They are very strong and can be used for large spans. They can also be used with a timber insert so that the timber appears to support the stonework above.

For small spans a single piece of solid stone may be used as a lintel

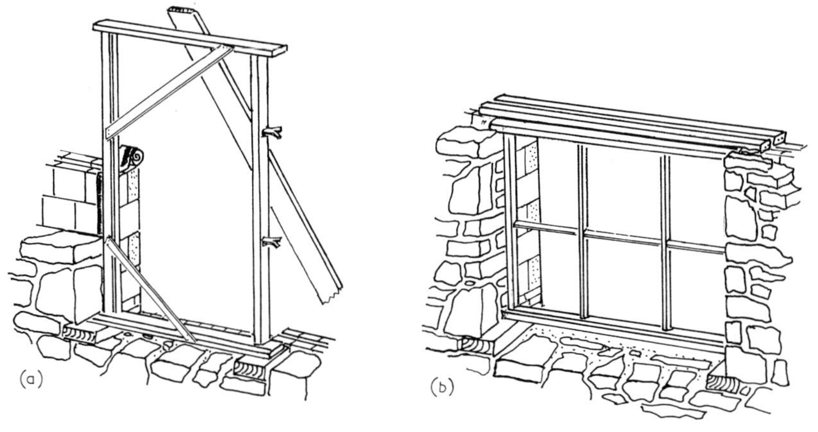

Fig 57 Building in door and window frames: (a) early stages in building a door frame; (b) window frame built in with concrete lintels in position of the blockwork skins. (Note: Sills not fitted until a later stage but allowed for by raising frames on wooden blocks bedded on sand)

(Plates 1 and 25), but these are difficult and expensive to obtain and extremely heavy to put in place. They are not satisfactory for large spans since manageable-size pieces would lack the required strength.

In the present construction solid timber lintels are going to be used to blend in with the original structure (*see* Plate 15) and these are suitable for most openings other than very large spans. The timber must be of well-seasoned hardwood such as oak since it has to resist the ravages of not only weather but also insect, plant and fungal attack for many years. It is further protected by treatment with a timber preservative which is best applied by immersing and leaving the lintel for as long as possible — at least a few days — in a bath of the liquid.

Such timber may be obtained as new timber specially sawn from a local saw mill, but a cheaper source is the familiar old derelict farm outbuilding. One of these should supply quite sufficient lintel material from the old roof purlins when they have been cleaned off and treated. Old railway sleepers also make excellent timber lintels.

Pre-cast concrete lintels are bedded in mortar on the blockwork to each side of the opening and the blockwork continued up to first floor level, two courses of brick being used over the lintels to level off to the block course. Wooden lintels are rested on the stonework and the stone built round and over them continuing any patterning that may have already been established.

For large open spans indoors where a load has to be supported above, for example the opening from the kitchen to the dining area shown on the plans, special steel girders termed *rolled steel joists* (RSJs) must be used as specified. Assistance will be required to get these into position and they are normally boxed in with wood below to disguise their ugly appearance. Fireproofing regulations stipulate what can be used to box in an RSJ and also require that they have to rest on fireproof pads. As

Plate 25 Old barn undergoing conversion to a home. Note the massive stone lintels

these regulations are rather complicated, they should be consulted in each individual case. The RSJs not only support the stone and blockwork above, but also carry the floor joists.

When all the lower floor frames are in place the walling is continued to first floor level where the joists are positioned on the internal block skin which must be perfectly level at this course.

8
First Floor Work and Roofing

Scaffolding

By the time the level of the first floor joists has been reached it will no longer be either safe or practical to work from trestles or cruder raised platforms. To continue building scaffolding will be required (Plate 26). This can be hired on a time basis, but the inexperienced should get instruction and assistance from the hire firm for its erection. Incorrectly assembled scaffolding can be a great danger not only to those working on it, but also to people below. It is also important to ensure that no pole comes into contact with any overhead electricity supply cable, the outer insulation of which can be quickly chafed by rubbing in the wind. Then somebody would be in for a nasty shock.

If possible try to obtain the modern lightweight alloy poles with easy fittings. These are much more manageable than old fashioned heavy steel scaffolding.

Demolition

If the building is unoccupied all the major demolition work is best carried out before digging out the foundations for the new extension. In this case building can proceed in an orderly manner and all the external and partition walls be completed to first floor level prior to receiving the joists. However, in the situation illustrated here, we have assumed that the dwelling is occupied and the lean-to kitchen extension in use. The major part of the building work has been carried on around this kitchen extension without directly interfering with it. At this stage however, it would be best to demolish this lean-to so that all the first floor joists can be laid. Once these have been fitted over the kitchen area they can be covered with polythene sheeting to provide a measure of weather protection until the roof is in place.

Fixing the Joists

Building regulations clearly define the maximum permissible span for timber joists laid at specific distances apart (as measured from centre to centre) and of various dimensions. To save on the cost of wood it is generally best to run the joists across the shortest span in any room. The most common distance between the centres of adjacent joists is 400mm

Plate 26 New home being built using a block and stone construction technique. Note the scaffolding for upper floor work

(16in). With this spacing, joists measuring 50mm x 175mm (2in x 7in) are completely adequate for spans of up to 3.95 metres (13ft). Alternatively, the depth of the joist may be reduced by using thicker timber, say 75mm x 150mm (3in x 6in), providing a similar maximum span. However, it is the depth of the joist rather than the thickness which provides the strength.

The joists may be fixed either directly on the blockwork or to the blockwork by means of joist hangers (Fig 58b). With direct fixing the joists must extend over the whole of a single skin of blocks. Thus, on partition walls, they must be positioned side by side and not end to end.

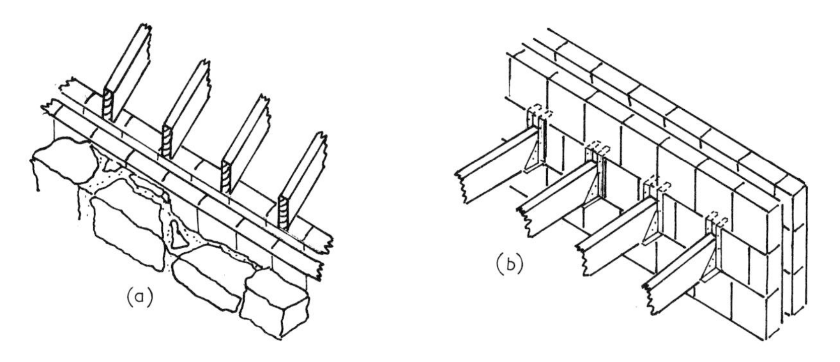

Fig 58 Fixing the joists: (a) direct fixing into internal blockwork skin; (b) fixing with joist hangers

With cavity walls the joists rest on the inner skin only and must not span the cavity otherwise moisture may penetrate (Fig 58). A coat of preservative must also be applied to the ends of the joists where they are embedded in the wall. The joists are held in position by layering two courses of brickwork between them and continuing the blockwork courses over the top. Where joist hangers are used, these are mortared and pinned directly into the blockwork at the appropriate height and the joists cut to size to fit between the walls rather than rest on them.

Trimming

Where an opening has to be made in the joists to accommodate a staircase a type of construction known as *trimming to openings* or simply *trimming* must be used (Fig 59). The opening is bordered by a joist known as a *trimmer joist* which is jointed between two joists termed *trimming joists*. These run the whole span between the walls. The trimmer then carries shorter joists from the opening to one wall, hence their name *trimmed joists*.

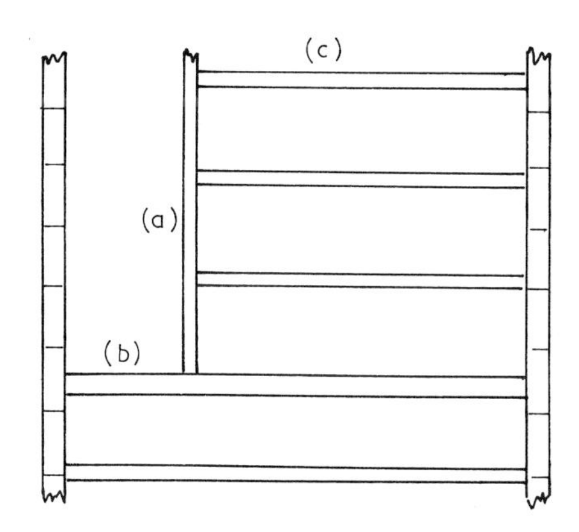

Fig 59 Trimming joists: (a) trimmer joist; (b) trimming joist; (c) trimmed joist

The two trimming joists have to carry a greater load than the normal joists therefore they are thicker, not deeper, which would complicate the ceiling construction. The trimmer is either hung between these by means of joist hangers, which is the simplest method, or jointed into them by various approved techniques requiring the skill of a joiner. The trimmed joists are connected to the trimmer by similar means.

In any room which has four walls, a joist is obviously needed at the wall ends where these run parallel to the joists. Do not build these tight against the walls but allow a gap of about 50mm (2in).

Strutting

As the widths of the spans increase, the joists tend to buckle and twist sideways under the load. This can be seen quite commonly in old cottages where the joists are exposed. It can be prevented by *strutting*. In *solid strutting* lengths of timber are nailed between the joists to hold them

Plate 27 Old beamed ceiling, cleaned and renovated

straight and together. Another form of strutting, *herring bone strutting*, can also be used but is more complicated and should only be tackled by a joiner.

If the joists are to be covered, strutting is an excellent way of strengthening the floor, but it does mar the appearance of an exposed-joist ceiling. Large spans were handled in old cottages by using massive beams across the rooms which acted as lintels and the joists were laid from the walls to these giving the traditional low beamed ceiling of old buildings (Plate 27). If suitable timber is available this is a perfectly satisfactory method of construction and in keeping with the character of the dwelling.

When the joists are fixed in place temporary boarding is placed over them to provide a working platform to continue construction of the internal walls. The permanent boarding of the floors is not carried out until the roofing felt is in place to weatherproof the building. The most popular choice for floorboarding is 150mm (6in) tongue-and-groove. When laying such boards, remember to leave a gap of approximately 13mm (½in) around the room to allow for expansion. (This gap will be masked by the wall finish and skirting boards.

Walling to the Eaves

It is now important to construct and felt the roof as quickly as possible to weatherproof the building, not only for the sake of the occupants but also to allow interior work to be carried out at times when the weather is too bad to allow outside building to continue. Since the roof is carried on the internal block skin, as soon as the upper floor windows have been built in, further work on the external stone face can be postponed until the roof has been sealed.

Building techniques to the eaves are the same as those described in the previous chapter, the height of the eaves being predetermined by those of the original building. In the example shown in the plans, provision for the erection of the lean-to roof would be made in the facework of the south wall when necessary.

The rafters are carried between the ridge board and the wall plates and the relative position of these determines the pitch of the roof (Fig 60). Since the position of the ridge board is strictly determined and the separation of the wall plates almost as strictly determined by the run of the internal block skin of the cavity wall, alteration of the pitch is only possible by adjusting the height of the wall plates above ground level. They should be set fractionally high to allow the rafters to be notched down onto them.

The wall plates are straight true timbers 100mm x 75mm (4in x 3in) which are bedded in mortar on the top of the internal skin of the

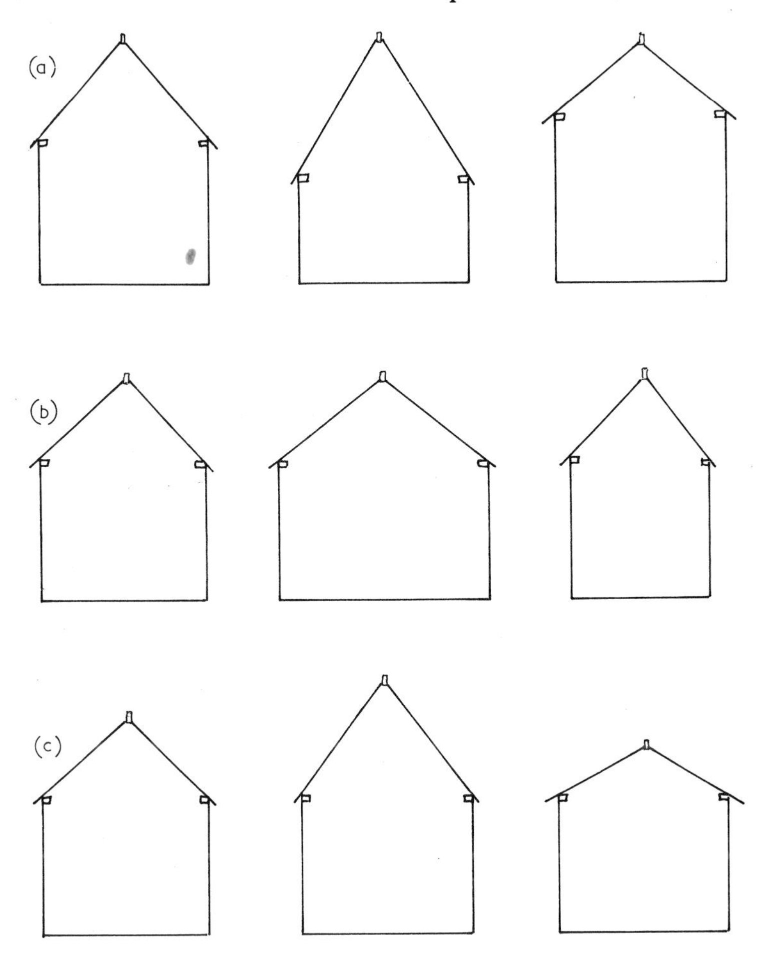

Fig 60 Roof pitch determined by relative positions of ridge and wall plates: (a) ridge fixed, wall plate height varied; (b) ridge fixed, distance between wall plates varied; (c) wall plates fixed, ridge height varied

Fig 61 Positioning the wall plates

blockwork. The easiest way to obtain their final correct height is to build the blockwork to a level so that when the wall plate is laid without mortar a rafter resting on it is in perfect alignment. Then, when the wall plate is bedded in mortar, it will be slightly higher and the rafters may be notched onto it.

The wall plates also serve to ensure that the roof will be set 'square' in the event of slight inaccuracies in the walling. If the eaves walls are not quite parallel, the wall plates are simply moved together or apart at their ends to compensate for this. The wall plates must be exactly the same distance apart throughout the entire length of the roof span (Fig 61).

The prospect of building the gable end (also known as the *pyke* or *pine* end) wall always seems to give the beginner nightmares until it is realised that the actual shape of the slope is not built until after the rafters are in position. The rafters then provide a building guide. The blocks are simply laid in a stepped fashion to the apex of the gable and the ridge board placed in position (Fig 62). No further blockwork is necessary until the rafters are in place and the roof basically self-supporting on the wall plate. When all the roof timbers are in place, the wall cavity is closed off by bricking across it and the stone and blockwork built up to the level of the rafters, both at the eaves and on the gable ends.

Roofs

Basic Forms

Roofs come in all shapes and sizes, and methods of construction vary considerably. Some are definitely beyond the capabilities of the average DIY enthusiast. Simpler types of roofing such as those shown in the plans may be tackled with a little assistance.

There are several ways of classifying roof form. The simplest way is to divide them into three groups according to shape: flat, curved and pitched. The main roof in the plans is of the *double pitched* type since it slopes outwards from the apex in two directions. The lower roof on the south wall is a *monopitch* or *lean-to* roof, having only a single slope.

In keeping with the original cottage and to give adequate room height in the upper floors, the double-pitched construction will be of the *purlin* type. This means that the rafter spans are strengthened by substantial timbers termed purlins which run between, and parallel to, the wall plate and ridge board beneath the rafters (Fig 63a). These are supported on the gable end walls. Ceiling joists are absent; instead the ceiling is formed by boarding across the rafters.

The purlin roof has been largely replaced these days by the *trussed rafter* roof (Fig 63b). Here each pair of rafters is obtained as a single prefabricated unit. These are then set directly on the wall plates and the ridge board as such dispensed with.

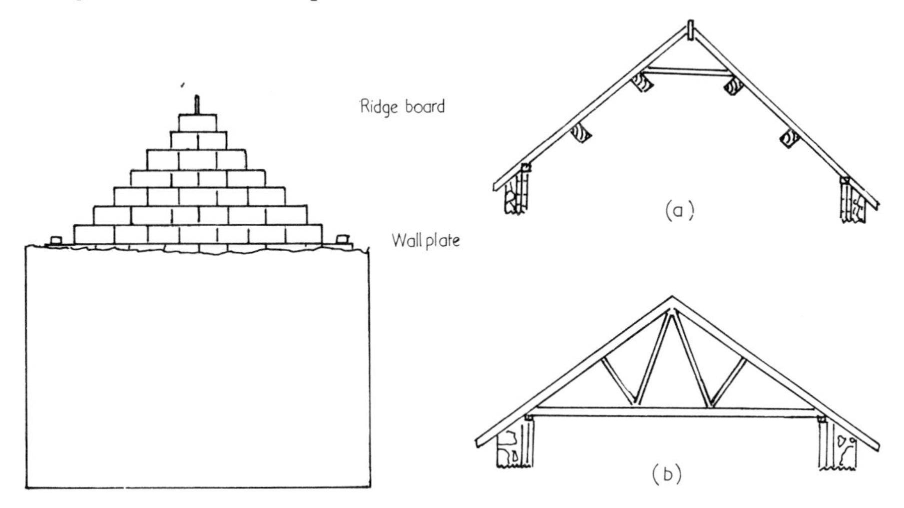

(Left) Fig 62 Positioning the ridge board on the gable end blockwork skin. *(Right)* Fig 63 Simple roof forms: (a) collared double purlin roof; (b) trussed rafter roof

Roof Construction

The Ridge Board

With the wall plates set in position, the next stage is to lay the rafters to the ridge board. The ridge board consists ideally of a single length of timber 175mm x 31mm (7in x 2in). However, if a single length cannot be obtained, then the portions should be jointed and bolted together. The ridge itself is not a supporting structure as far as the roof is concerned, it simply enables the rafters to be aligned and fixed together and is itself carried by the rafters. At the gable end the ridge is set on the new blockwork to the required finished height and is carried well out from this to accommodate the stone facework and overhang. The other end of the ridge will abut the chimney stack on the old gable and on no account must timbers be set into the chimney flues. To overcome the problem of temporary support for the ridge until the rafters are in place, a wooden block can be nailed to the stack and removed at a later date.

Rafters

It will by now come as no surprise to learn that rafter dimensions and spacing are also subject to various regulations. To comply with these, the timbers most commonly used are 100mm x 50mm (4in x 2in), placed 400mm (16in) apart from centre to centre. The rafters are erected in pairs, one to each pitch, to prevent distortion of the ridge board. They are notched onto the wall plate with a 'bird's mouth' V-joint about 25mm (¾in) deep. At the ridge the rafters are cut to an angle to fit flush to the ridge (Fig 64). The rafters are cross-nailed to both the ridge board and wall plate and are cut long enough to project out over the eaves to carry the weatherboarding.

The first two pairs of rafters erected are those at the ends of the ridge board to the inside of the gable end walls. These pairs are set 30mm (1in) away from the walls and the positions of the remaining rafters taken from these, working from each end towards the middle of the roof alternately. The last pair of rafters — those to the outside of the new gable end, are not put into position until they can be correctly aligned outside the stone facework. Around the chimney stack, struts are inserted between the rafters, and the stack chiselled out to accommodate a flashing where necessary. Any rafters which only run as far as such struts would be termed *trimmed rafters (see Trimming,* page 121).

Purlins

The purlins are stout timbers providing additional support for the rafters and roof covering. On wide spans, those exceeding 3 metres (10ft) between the eaves, it is advisable to insert two purlins for each pitch. The purlins are formed from timbers generally in the order of 200mm x 100mm (8in x 4in), and again building regulations define maximum spans for various timber sizes.

The purlins are set into position on the gable ends and built into the blockwork, the lower of the two purlins first. They are turned through an angle to bring the narrower edge flush to the bottom of the rafters which are cross-nailed to the purlin (Fig 64). The two purlins are positioned so that they divide the rafter span into three equal sections.

To resist the tendency of the roof to splay under the weight of the tiles, the rafters should be *collared.* The collars are timbers, usually of the same dimensions as the rafters, nailed between the two rafters in each pair at the level of the upper purlins and trimmed flush with the slope of the rafter (Fig 63). Although not as effective as *ties,* which are positioned lower down, they do allow increased room height.

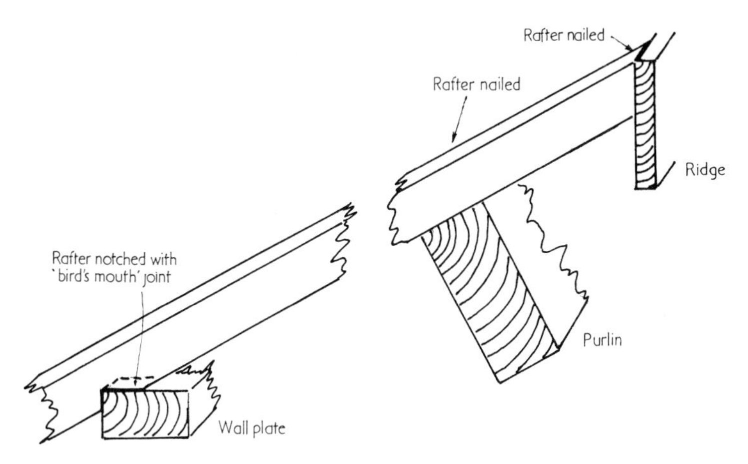

Fig 64 Fixing rafters to wall plates, ridge board and purlin. (Rafters jointed only on the wall plate but cross nailed to all the members)

Roof Covering

With the main roof timbers in place the roof can quickly be felted and battened to weatherproof the interior of the building and the actual tiling and roof finishing left to a later date when all the facework is completed.

Felting

Felting is a job which can easily be undertaken by the do-it-yourselfer.

Since an open ceiling method of roof construction is being used, there will be no loft space which can be insulated against heat loss. Thus insulation must be put down at the level of the rafters. While it is possible to pour granular insulation products between the rafters as these are boarded up from the inside, it is far easier to incorporate insulation and felting at the same time by buying roof felt already backed with insulating material. This can be obtained in rolls from most builders' merchants.

The felt is nailed to the rafters with special wide-headed galvanised felt nails and should have a minimum overlap of 75mm (3in) at the horizontal joints and 150mm (6in) at the vertical joints. It should also be allowed to sag slightly between the rafters to provide a 'gutter' to shed any water penetrating the roof covering. Allow a generous overlap at the ends of the rafters so that it can be nailed over the fascia board when this is erected.

Working from the ridge down saves the felt from accidental puncture. However, it is a lot easier to work from the eaves to the ridge, overlapping the ridge with a single piece of felt at the finish. Any punctures should be patched with a generous piece of felt (not backed with insulation) stuck down with an appropriate adhesive. Patching is an arduous job. I vividly remember having completed a felting job and returning the following day to discover that the young boys who lived in the house plus their friends had spent a happy evening firing arrows and other missiles through the felt! It would have taken a week to patch all the punctures, so the battens had to be removed and the roof re-felted. No matter how careful *you* are, you cannot always count on other people, or at least their kids, to be the same!

Battening

The battens, which are also known as laths, are the means by which the slates or tiles are hung. They also help to secure the felt. Rough lengths of timber 38mm x 19mm (1¼in x ⅝in) are used for the battens, although they can be thicker for wider rafter spacings. They are attached to the rafters with galvanised nails and any joins should be centred on the rafters. Roofing contractors rarely saw the battens but use a special tool known as a *slater's axe* to both chop the battens to size and nail them in position (Fig 65).

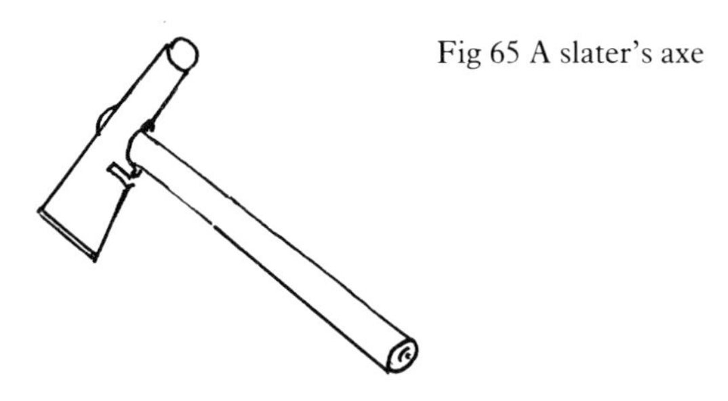

Fig 65 A slater's axe

The batten spacing is very important since it has to be compatible with the type of tile or slate being used for the covering. For new tiles manufacturers generally recommend a certain spacing, but if you are matching your new roof to the old one by using the same materials then the old roof will show you the necessary batten positions. If working with old slates of unequal size which are laid in diminishing courses (*see* Plate 18), then the batten spacing will be reduced progressively from the eaves to the ridge.

Tiling and Slating

This is extremely heavy work requiring a degree of fitness and agility not generally encountered in those unused to such work. Although the individual tiles or slates may not seem heavy, transporting half a dozen at a time up the ladder to the roof and laying them correctly is quite a different matter when the trip has to be made a hundred or more times over! For this reason alone it could be well worth subcontracting this part of the work.

The determined person can obtain the best instruction by examining the existing roof, bearing in mind that you work from the eaves to the ridge in a diagonal manner so that the tiles are overlapped both at their heads and sides. The course of tiles at the ridge must be a full course and the ridge is overlapped by special ridge tiles which are bedded in mortar. The end tiles on the ridge are tilted to direct water back onto the roof away from verges and the facework.

Where the vent pipe protrudes through the roof water must be excluded by fitting a special rubber-collared tile around the pipe.

Roof Finishes

Weatherboarding

The weatherboarding which carries the gutters along the eaves, where it is known also as the *fascia board*, is fitted to the rafters which must be cut to a vertical face to receive it (Fig 66). The fascia board is generally 150mm x 25mm (6in x 1in) with a groove along the back to take the *soffit*, which seals the roof against the entry of small birds. The fascia is nailed to the cut end of each rafter then the roofing felt brought over the top and nailed in place. The tiles overlap the fascia board shedding water directly into the gutters mounted beneath (Fig 66). The soffit is fitted into the groove on the fascia board and nailed to the bottom of the rafters which have been cut to provide a suitable horizontal surface and held down onto the top of the stonework by small pieces of batten nailed to the rafters. (Fig 66). The gutter brackets can be fixed to the fascia board to fall to the downpipes either before or after the fascia is fitted.

It is worth remembering that too large an overhang will provide a sheltered position for house martins to construct their nests with the attendant nuisance, if not damage. I consider it easier to adopt an alternative method of fixing the fascia board as follows: a line is strung along the rafters and these are cut to present a vertical face approximately

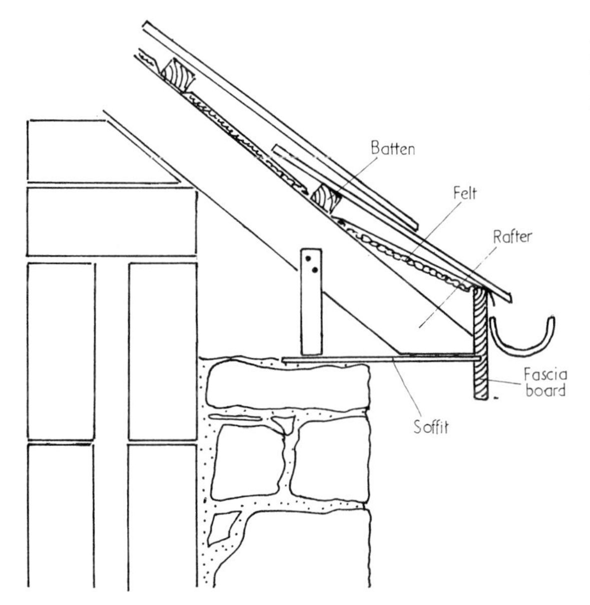

Fig 66 Section at the eaves to illustrate one method of fixing weatherboarding

45mm (1½in) outside the stone facework. The stonework is then completed and levelled off with a course of roofing slate in such a way that the slates protrude from the wall to the bottom of the cut ends of the rafters (Fig 67). Since work above the slates will not show, the rest of the building work between the rafters can be finished in brick. Plain boarding 175mm x 25mm (7in x 1in) is used for the fascia and simply nailed to the cut ends of the rafters and the felt and tiles overlapped to the guttering as previously. The slates now replace the function of the soffit (Fig. 67).

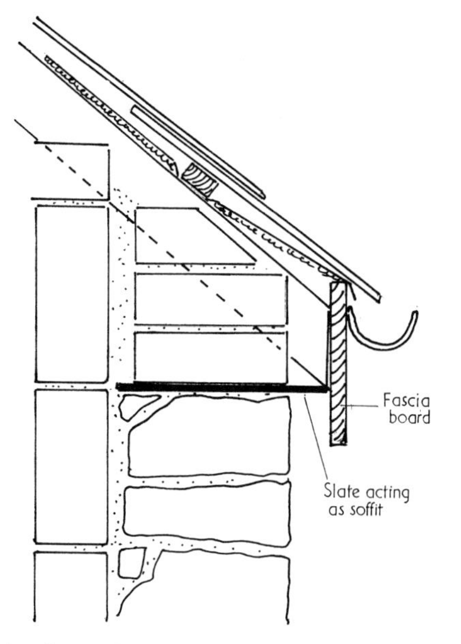

Fig 67 Alternative method of finishing at the eaves

At the gable ends the weatherboarding is termed the *barge board* and this was often ornately carved in days past. The barge board carries no guttering but simply serves to provide a finish to the roof. The ridge and purlins are cut flush to the last rafter and the barge board nailed directly to this. The felt and tiles are brought over the board and bedded on a mortar fillet which raises their outside edge on the verges so directing water back onto the roof. A soffit is simply nailed to the underside of the rafter to fit flush between the barge board and stonework.

Flashings

Wherever the roof joins a vertical face, for example a lean-to roof against the eaves or around a chimney stack, the join must be protected by a flashing to prevent the entry of water. The traditional flashing material is lead although other, cheaper, products are now available. Whatever material you choose, the method of fixing is the same. The flashing must be firmly bedded with mortar into the vertical face of the building and dressed out a minimum distance of 150mm (6in) over the tiles.

Around chimney stacks the flashing is usually stepped to reduce the amount of lead used and, whereas this is a fairly simple process with brickwork which offers a regular sequence of joints, stonework presents greater problems. Often it will be necessary to remove larger stones and replace them completely to enable the flashing to be mortared in place. Therefore, whenever building with random stone, it is best to build the flashing in position as you go rather than attempting to insert it later. This applies to the lean-to roof on the south wall in the plans.

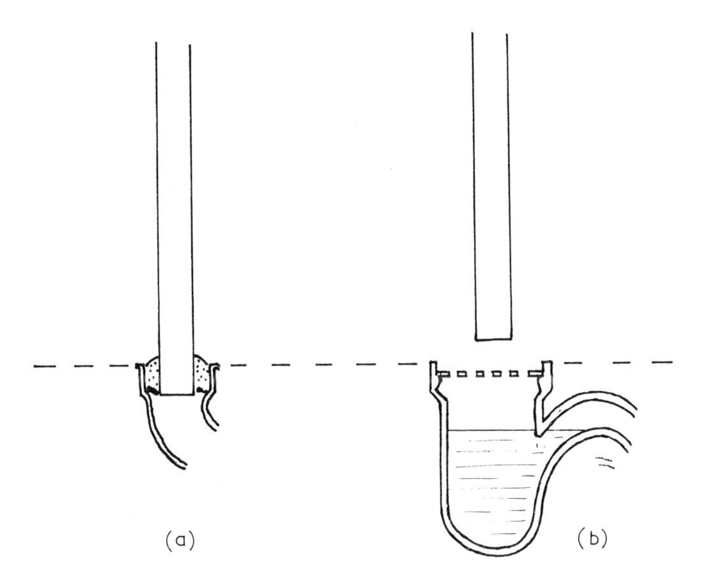

Fig 68 Method of connecting downpipes to the drains: (a) sealed connection; (b) open drain pot

Guttering
The gutters, which direct rainwater from the roof to the downpipes, are fixed with brackets on the fascia boarding at the eaves of the building. They can either be fixed level or at a slight fall to the downpipes which, for small roof areas, may be located at one end only of the building.

Guttering, together with its special fittings, can be obtained in a variety of shapes and materials. PVC guttering is now undoubtedly the most popular: it is fairly cheap, lightweight, easy to fix and requires no maintenance, although it does need frequent support along its length. The downpipe supports should be held by screws into plugs fitted in the mortar joints of the facework and extend into the head of the drainpipe. The connection is then sealed with mortar (Fig 68).

9

Internal Work

By this time the basic shell should be complete and the structure taking on a finished look from the outside. Inside, however, the job is far from complete and progress will seem slow since the remaining jobs take a lot of time with little outwardly to show for it. Clients usually tend to fall out with builders at this stage since they become impatient to have the work finished and the workmen gone.

If carrying out the work yourself with the help of subcontractors, it will be at this stage that the major assistance will be required with several different tradesmen working together in the house: plasterers, plumbers, electricians and carpenters. With a small extension the place could become very overcrowded.

Plastering

I would like to stress that if you have had no previous experience of plastering, employ a plasterer! Plastering an extension is *not* a DIY project but a professional job learned by years of experience in the trade. The skill and techniques cannot be described in a book such as this, and since the plaster provides the important final finish to the work, you cannot afford for the job to be amateurish. Most plasterers regard their role, to a great extent, as one of correcting the defects and mistakes in the building work! The DIY builder is very likely to have made many of these and will require the skill of a professional to cover them up, rather than making things worse by heroically having a go himself.

One job that is normally handled by the plasterer, however, *can* be carried out by the do-it-yourselfer. This is adding the finishes to the ground floor solid floors whether they are to be of cement-screed or tiles.

Flooring

If the ground floor covering is to be the same throughout then the cement screed will be a constant thickness, usually about 50mm (2in). But should various different finishes be required, perhaps quarry tiles are to be laid in the kitchen, then the thickness of the screed will have to be adjusted to accommodate this. In such instances it is always best to lay the full screed floors first and bring the tiles or wood block floors up to this finished level afterwards. If polystyrene floor insulation is to be included this is also put in place at this stage, the polystyrene sheets being laid directly onto the subfloor and the 50mm (2in) screed put over the top (*see* Fig 33).

Cement Screed

Not only must the screed be level and not crack but it should also bond well to the concrete subfloors. The mix used is therefore kept fairly dry to minimise shrinkage and either bonding additives are incorporated in it or the subfloor wetted to improve adhesion. To obtain a true level throughout the room, battens are set in mortar to the true finished level dividing the room into manageable bays. The screed is then laid in the bays and levelled off using the straight edge on the screeding battens (Fig 69). The battens are removed as the work progresses. The surface finish is made with a steel floating trowel and the screed should be given ample time to set and harden before any further covering is applied.

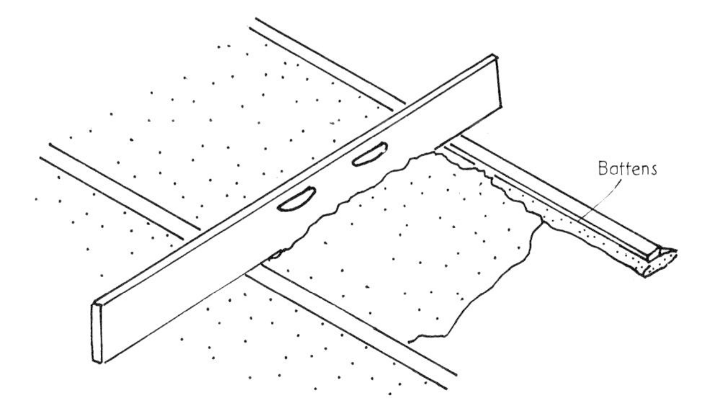

Fig 69 Laying the floor screed using screeding battens

In some places, for example in external doorways, the flooring must continue across the wall-cavity. To achieve this, pieces of thin roofing slate are first laid across the cavity and the screed carried through the opening on the slate at the required level.

Stone and Clay Tiles

Hard tiles, such as quarry tiles, generally have a considerable depth themselves (up to 30mm) and these can be laid in a mortar bed directly onto the subfloor. As with the screed floors, battens are set into mortar to provide the guides for the finished level and the tiles laid in bays. To give a good bond to the subfloor a 1 part cement to 3 parts sand mix is used at a wetter consistency than the screed.

Tiles are laid from the centre of the room out towards the walls. Not only does this ensure that a line of cut tiles does not appear in the body of the room, but it also means that the rough edges of such cut tiles can be hidden by the skirting boards. The tiles themselves are not butted flush together but a small joint left between them to be grouted in later. This joint must be maintained at a constant thickness and thin strips of wood are used as spacers and removed later.

Cutting stone and clay tiles may present some problems. It is worth hiring a mechanical stone cutter to cut stone tiles. These are portable, easy to handle and give a good finish to the work. Quarry tiles, however, cannot be cut with these owing to their hardness and must either be taken to a firm specialising in such work or else 'nibbled' to size by hand. If the cut edge is to be concealed then hand finishing is quite satisfactory and the technique is described in Fig 70, working a little of the tile at a time.

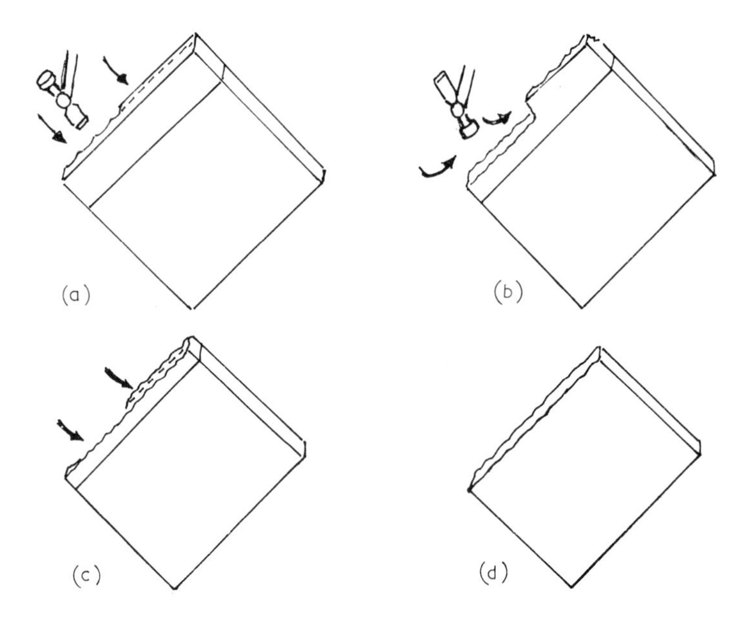

Fig 70 Stages in progressively cutting quarry tiles by hand with a light pin hammer

Grouting-in the joints once the floor has set may present some difficulties since the tile surface must be kept clean. Tiles with a smooth polished surface, as quarry tiles, are easier to grout than rougher textured surfaces. For smooth tiles, a wettish grouting mix is simply brushed into the joints with a soft broom then the floor is immediately sprinkled with sawdust and this swept clean. The sawdust absorbs all the moisture from the mix and cleans off the surface of the tiles, but on no account allow the grout to dry beforehand. With rougher stone surfaces the sawdust technique does not seem to work quite so well and it may be necessary to grout each joint carefully by hand with a dryish mix, cleaning off any spills as you go.

Flexible Tiles
Thermoplastic, linoleum and cork tiles should be bonded with an appropriate adhesive onto a screed finish according to the manufacturers' instructions.

Carpentry

If you have managed to tackle the roof timbers successfully there is no reason why you should not be able to do the rest of the necessary timber work with the possible exception of constructing a staircase. One thing to bear in mind is that there will be a lot of time-consuming work involved, so if time is at a premium then get the assistance of a carpenter for specific jobs.

Matchboarding Ceilings and Walls
In the open ceiling type of construction described earlier for the upper floors, there is no loft space and instead the ceiling is formed by wooden boarding nailed across the rafters. A special type of tongue-and-grooved board with bevelled edges 100mm (4in) wide, called matchboard, is used for this purpose. The boards are fixed in runs from the walls up to the ridge with the groove uppermost so that the tongue of the next board may be slotted into it. The tongue of the first board should be removed before it is nailed and the grooves of each board opened up in turn by running a short length of matchboard along them before they are fitted in place. This ensures that the grooves are clear and will easily accept the next board without risking damaging it with undue hammering.

The nailing may be 'hidden', with the nails driven at an angle through the lower portion of the groove and punched in, or else it can be done directly through the face of the board onto each rafter. The joints in the boards must be centred on a rafter and the purlins and collar timbers are left exposed.

It is important to remember that if the roof has not been insulated at the time of felting then insulation must accompany the matchboarding. Where no insulation is incorporated with matchboarding, damp problems sometimes occur as water vapour in the warm internal atmosphere rises and condenses in the cold space between the matchboarding and roofing felt, where it remains trapped. As a precautionary measure to prevent this, polythene sheeting should be pinned behind the matchboarding on the roof side so that any moisture in the air is prevented from entering the cold space beneath the rafters and so remains as vapour.

Close liaison with the electrician will be necessary while the ceiling is being boarded. The wiring for the ring main must be laid behind the matchboarding and provision for electrical fittings and points made as the boarding proceeds.

Matchboarding on walls to produced a panelled effect follows the same principles, once a framework has been built to carry the boards. The frame is generally constructed out of 50mm x 25mm (2in x 1in) softwood screwed or nailed to the wall with steel pins. On badly misshapen old walls it is essential that the framework does not follow the line of the wall but runs straight and remains vertical. This, and other forms of panelling, provide an excellent means of disguising such poor walls.

Flooring

The method of fixing the upper floor timbers has already been described in Chapter 8. However, if the joists are to be enclosed with a plasterboard ceiling below, it is necessary to leave floorboard traps (short lengths of timber from which the tongue has been removed) screwed down in appropriate places to allow access to the wiring. Here again an electrician should be consulted.

Doors

Modern lightweight hollow internal doors can be bought to fit standard frames, but these seem very much out of place in an old cottage. Traditional ledged, braced and battened doors and simple frames can be built to fit by most handymen and are much more in keeping with the character of an old dwelling.

Matchboarding is used for the door face which is nailed onto three horizontal 100mm x 25mm (4in x 1in) ledges strengthened by two diagonal braces on the same timber (Fig 71). To prevent drooping, the braces slope upwards from the hanging edge when the door is hung.

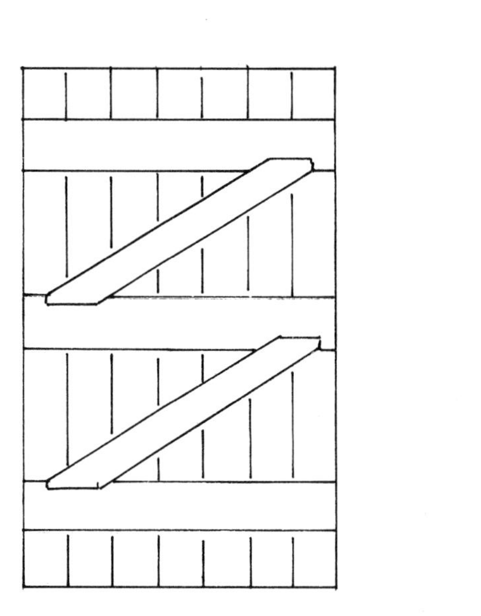

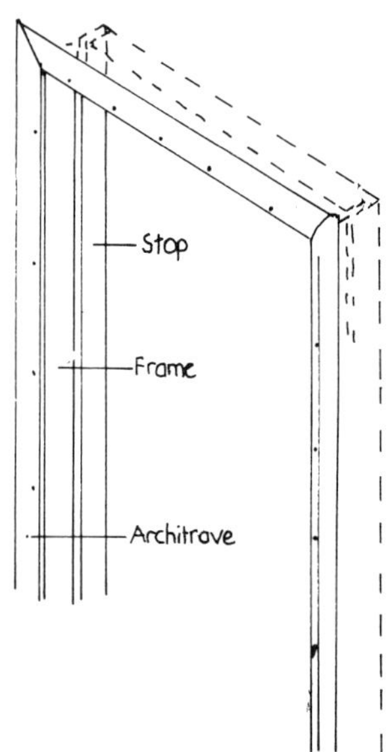

(Left) Fig 71 A ledged, braced and battened door. *(Right)* Fig 72 A simple door frame for an internal partition wall

Hanging is done with long strap or tee hinges attached to the top and bottom ledges. To increase the strength of the door the braces should be jointed to the ledges. A latch is the traditional ironmongery for this type of door.

The frame consists of 100mm x 25mm (4in x 1in) softwood around the opening to which is nailed a 25mm x 10mm (1in x 3/8in) strip on the non-opening, external side of the frame and against which the door is held closed (Fig 72). The door surround is finished off with a moulded architrave which covers the junction of the frame with the wall and is pinned to the frame. This architrave can be bought direct from most timber merchants and needs only to be cut to length, mitred at the corners and fixed in position.

External doors will need to be of heavier construction and should be bought to fit the standard frames already in place. These are usually hung on concealed butt hinges, or better still rising butt hinges which help to reduce draughts when the door is closed.

Skirting Boards

The skirting boards protect the base of the wall from mechanical damage and also provide a convenient means of hiding wiring, cut edges etc. A wide variety of styles and sizes exists and the choice is purely personal. The boarding is nailed into wooden lugs inserted in the raked out joints of the blockwork, and it is mitred at the corners. When nailing be careful to avoid the wiring behind.

Internal Sills

The internal wooden window sills should be set into position before plastering so that the plaster can be finished to the board. In the type of wall construction and frame placement suggested, the internal sills will be the depth of the block walls and cavity, 250mm (10in), which is considerably deeper than in modern houses. Timber merchants, however, do supply window boarding to accommodate this width, though it may have to be ordered in advance.

The board is simply cut to shape and the back of the board slotted into the groove on the base of the window frame. The front edge is then nailed into the blockwork. If the sills tilt inwards slightly the front edge of the board can be raised by a strip of batten set flush to the face of the blocks. (This will be hidden by the plasterwork later.)

Cupboards, Shelving and Units

Building kitchen units, bookshelves, and the like is well covered in other books dealing with DIY carpentry so it will not be discussed here. One point, however, is worth noting. New timber is very expensive, old secondhand furniture often ridiculously cheap. It may be cheaper to buy an old cupboard or bookcase and take it apart for the wood rather than buy new timber. The quality is likely to be better too.

Home Electrics

Whilst adding new wiring and replacing old wiring systems is certainly not beyond the scope of the DIY handyman, they are outside the scope of this book, and are adequately covered in others (*see* Bibliography). All wiring generally needs to be replaced in an old house. This should be done at the same time as the new wiring is put into the extension. Modern features such as trip switches can be incorporated into the circuits. It is also worth considering moving the meter so that it can be read from outside the house.

Glazing

The prospect of glazing the windows in a new extension can be daunting, especially if windows with many small panes have been installed. Most people will have had experience of replacing only the odd broken pane in the past and will naturally multiply the time this took by the number of panes needed in the extension, so arriving at a horrifying figure for the man-hours involved. But this is wrong since most of the time taken in replacing a pane is spent in chipping away the old hard putty. In any case you will quickly speed up after the first few panes.

The glass can be ordered cut to size (remember to allow a small clearance all round) from the local suppliers, together with putty and sprigs. The putty is worked in the hands until it is very soft and malleable. Then holding it in a ball in one hand, line the inside of the frame with the putty pressing it off the ball with your thumb onto the woodwork in a continuous, even flow. The glass is pressed firmly into this and held in place with sprigs or panel pins nailed into the frame. Note that the putty itself does not hold the glass firm but is there merely to provide a weatherproof seal. If you forget the pins you are likely to have another large glazing job on your hands the next time a jumbo jet passes overhead!

After pinning, the exterior is sealed with putty covering the sprigs and the job smoothed up and trimmed inside and out with a putty knife. If the putty tends to stick to the knife and pull away from the glass, keep the knife wetted with cold water. Do not attempt to paint until the putty is well hardened; and do mention to any young children around that the putty is not some sort of new-fangled play dough to be stripped off for their own devices.

Painting and Papering

Since I am probably one of the world's most reluctant and ineffectual painters and decorators, I feel that the only advice I can honestly give is on how to avoid doing these jobs. I consider that women make far better painters, having a different type of patience than men and better motivation to have the work done exactly right. So marry a wife who enjoys painting and keep telling her what an excellent job she is making of it — at the same time stressing that you are, unfortunately, tied up with other, more strenuous, aspects of the construction!

Wall Tiles

Ceramic tiles are commonly used as splash backs in both the kitchen and bathroom and may be fixed to both walls and window sills. They are best fitted onto the cement render before the finishing plaster coat is applied and this is particularly important where fairly thick tiles are used. The golden rule for tiling is to start at the exact centre of the area to be tiled and work out to the corners so that the cut tiles are less obvious.

Ceramic tiles are fixed with an appropriate tile cement according to the manufacturer's instructions and then grouted in with tile grout applied as a slurry and washed in. Special tile cutters can be bought at most hardware and DIY shops complete with detailed instructions on how to use them. Modern tiles generally have spacer lugs at their edges which ensure an even joint for grouting. If these are absent then slips of cardboard should be used between the tiles as they are laid to maintain an even joint. Unlike brickwork and blockwork the tiles are not laid in a bonded manner but directly above each other. Therefore it is essential to ensure that the first tile set in place is perfectly positioned.

To tile internal window sills the cavity is first closed with pieces of slate and a cement screed window sill cast in position on the slate. Once this has hardened the tiles can be fixed in place. In this case use finishing tiles which are rounded on one side on the edge and work in from these so that the cut tiles are against the frame.

Plumbing

As with plastering and wiring, I consider that it is worthwhile subcontracting the plumbing work to a professional plumber who has the necessary tools as well as the expertise to carry out the work quickly and correctly and deal with any serious problems.

10

Home Protection and Improvement

Part II of this book has been devoted to the building of a modest extension to a small stone cottage. For many people the house or cottage may not require extension, the basic shell being big enough but it may need considerable renovation if it has been neglected for any length of time, or altering to suit personal requirements. This section covers renovation and also the improvement or conversion of outbuildings, perhaps to provide a garage, storeroom, workshop or playroom to relieve the pressure on space within the house itself.

So here we are concerned with the improvement of existing stone buildings, rather than new building in stone. Many of the basic building techniques will be those already described in Part II and this section should be read before undertaking any major alterations.

Internal alterations are not generally subject to planning permission or building regulations but should of course follow sound building practice if only for the sake of safety. Contrary to popular belief, building regulations are not designed to be a bureaucratic nuisance but to make buildings safer. So, even without regulations to guide you, do not set to and demolish unwanted walls without first considering their function as an integral part of the building. When replacing floors think about the spacing of the joists. If re-roofing with a different form of roof covering, bear in mind that the roof timbers will have to support it, and so on.

If you are undertaking grant-aided improvements remember that certain standards will have to be met. Details of these have been given in Chapter 3.

Demolition

Before doing any demolition it is extremely important to have a thorough knowledge of the construction of the building. Ascertain whether it was originally built on mass construction or frame construction principles. If mass constructed then the gable end walls are the main supporting units for the roof. If it is of frame construction then the timber frame in the eaves walls is the most important supporting member (*see* Chapter 1). Alterations involving the supporting walls or frame must be made with care and understanding to avoid seriously weakening the whole building.

Similarly be wary of buildings to which extensions have previously been added. The original gable end may have been skilfully enclosed and now appear as an internal wall, as with the extension described in Part II. But it still remains as the major supporting wall for both the original cottage and the new extension. Before breeching internal walls be certain that they do not have a particular function with respect to the whole building.

The majority of old stone buildings were erected as shelters which did not have to satisfy the needs and requirements of the present time and, more important, did not house the array of perishable possessions associated with modern living. Thus, modern strip foundations will be absent. Instead the building will be erected directly on the ground using the bedrock as a natural foundation. Indeed in some instances a rock outcrop may even form part of the lower wall itself. Loads from the wall and roof were further spread by tapering the walls on the inside from a broad base built out of massive stones to a narrower wall composed of smaller stones towards the eaves. It is not uncommon to discover a difference of 250mm (10in) in wall thickness from ground level to the eaves.

The walls themselves will lack both a cavity and a damp proof course and, while the thickness of the walls prevents dampness penetrating through them to the interior, rising damp will always present problems. The gap between the stone faces of the walls is often loosely filled with rubble and lime and this can create difficulties when making new openings.

Get to know your property intimately before you even start *planning* to demolish anything. Buildings are built from the ground upwards and ideally demolition should proceed in the reverse order. However, this is rarely practical, so a compromise approach must be adopted, bearing in mind a golden rule of demolition; whatever you knock down is supporting something above which will also fall unless adequately supported beforehand.

Enlarging existing openings in random stonework presents greater difficulties than in brickwork due to the absence of true coursing. Generally the openings have to be made far larger than required and rebuilt to the required size. If making new openings make sure that you know what is both above and around the proposed openings. Strip off existing plasterwork and carefully examine the stonework to ensure that there are no huge stones likely to project into the proposed opening.

In many old properties the plasterwork will have degenerated through time and damp and in the long run its total removal will be less bothersome than continually patching it up. If you hack it off this will also show you the character of the stonework and reveal the true state of any electrical wiring. Re-render and plaster the whole room, if you wish, when the structural alterations are complete.

Demolition invariably produces mountains of material, but do not simply look upon it as waste. Certain items are best disposed of, for example old plaster, tin sheeting, and wiring; but look critically at the supposedly unsound timbers you take out. The damage may be confined to the ends which can be sawn off, the worm holes may only be superficial and the timbers treated rather than discarded (*see* Plate 27). Besides, if the fireplace is going to be restored it will devour wood quite uncritically so, at the very least, you will be throwing away free fuel.

Roofing materials are generally re-usable and should be removed with care and stacked out of the way. Even damaged stone roofing flags make an excellent decorative paving material for the garden or terrace.

The most important demolition material is the actual building stone, firstly because it is the perfect match for doing any new stonework on the property and, secondly, since it has been used already for building you know it can be used again. Flagstones on the kitchen floor, old slate working tops, stone steps and sills may also all be used again, perhaps in different roles, either in the house or garden. They would all cost a fortune to reproduce from freshly quarried stone.

The demolition of old stonework can be as slow a process as the actual building work. The stones should be removed one by one as far as possible and cleaned, sorted and stored as described previously. The first stone is generally the most difficult to remove, and particularly so in well-matched and tied stonework. Look critically over the whole structure and select a stone that not only looks as though it may come out fairly easily but will allow free access to neighbouring stones. A 'chinked' stone or one surrounded by a large mortar joint is often a good one to start with. Clear out the joint first using the lump hammer and cold chisel, then work the stone loose by levering it with the bar.

Whenever making any opening in the eaves wall the joists or rafters *must* be supported first. This can be done either with special jacks, which can be hired, or with stout timbers. These are positioned inside the building beneath each joist, remembering to leave sufficient working space between the support and the wall. Dust sheeting can be pinned to the supports to reduce the amount of mess within the room.

Avoid taking risks with yourself or the building during demolition work. Do not leave unsupported stonework or open stairwells at the end of the day. The curious trespasser may well be *your own child*. Use safety equipment: goggles to protect the eyes from dust and flying chips of stone, a mask to prevent the inhalation of lime dust, stout boots and a safety helmet to soften the blow from falling stones. If dismantling a chimney stack use correctly mounted scaffolding or *cripples* (in the form of specially shaped wooden platforms) around the stack. It is not wise to try to work off a ladder.

Renovation and Protection

The single most important renovation project in an old stone dwelling is the protection of the building and its contents from the ravages of damp, pests and disease and the cure of any damage already caused by these agents. Failure to undertake such work immediately puts any new extension and interior decoration at risk. The major protection should be directed against dampness in the basic structure. Most of the other problems are of a secondary nature, themselves the result of the damp.

Dampness occurs in old buildings in two main ways. It may rise by capillary action from the ground through the walls and floors, or it may penetrate the structure from outside. Both possibilities must be considered and any faults corrected *before* other renovation work is started.

Rising Damp

In modern building rising damp is prevented by the inclusion of a DPC and DPM in the walls and floors respectively. These are lacking in old buildings and this problem must be overcome in some other way. In old brick buildings it is possible to cut into the brickwork and insert a mechanical damp barrier like the DPC used in modern building. This will cure the problem of rising damp, but it could aggravate the problem of penetrating damp by causing a buildup of water on top of the DPC. In this instance both causes of damp must be considered together. With random stonework it is quite impractical to consider the insertion of a DPC. Some other method of damp proofing is required. Nowadays several approved electrical and chemical methods of countering rising damp are available. None of these are really suitable work for an

Plate 28 Electrolytic damp proofing *Rentokil Ltd*

amateur and I would recommend that a reputable firm is employed to do the job. It may seem expensive, but the long term guarantee provided does much to up the re-sale value of the property.

If an electro-osmotic method is adopted, which requires the insertion of a copper strip into the wall (Plate 28), insist on a decent standard of finished workmanship from the firm, especially if the stonework will be left exposed to view. Ensure that the old mortar is removed between the stones first, the strip well-bedded and the joints then neatly pointed up afterwards to the style *you* require.

Dampness rising through the floors is generally easier to combat. This can certainly be undertaken by the unskilled person and does not necessarily require the floor to be removed beforehand. If the room height will permit it, a polythene membrane may simply be laid on the existing floor and the screed finish laid on this. If not, the existing floor will need to be removed and a new floor laid after excavating to the correct depth, as previously described for the new floors in an extension. In all cases the DPM must be set lower than the damp proofing mechanism in the walls, otherwise the moisture from the floors will simply be transmitted to the walls.

Perhaps the easiest cure for damp in floors is simply to coat the floor with an appropriate bituminous paint and then apply the floor finish required directly onto this when it has dried. However this may not be possible if the old floor is cracked or uneven. Further cracking can fracture the skin of paint and allow damp through, and if the floor is uneven, problems will be encountered when applying the final finish.

Penetrating Damp

Moisture may enter the building in obvious places where the weatherproof envelope has become damaged, such as the roof covering, and also in less obvious places such as damaged flashing. However, direct penetration of the walls of the building itself is more of a problem. In many instances it is not possible to cure, but only to control it.

Because water continuously evaporates from a wall surface, as well as being absorbed by it, moisture levels within the wall fluctuate markedly according to climatic conditions. But as long as the evaporation rate exceeds the absorption rate solid walls will not transmit damp. Stone walls with a minimum thickness of 500mm (20in), even those built from fairly porous stone, very rarely become damp on the inside through moisture penetrating from the exterior. This is because, despite our British weather, evaporation is rapid enough to halt the inward penetration of water due to rain.

Serious dangers can occur if the exterior of the building is unnecessarily treated with a waterproof render. Although these reduce or prevent penetration, they also reduce or prevent evaporation. In the absence of a DPC to prevent rising damp such render will immediately worsen or even create a damp problem. This is because considerable moisture is generated within the home, especially in the kitchen and bathroom. Without adequate ventilation, perhaps because draughts are excluded by double glazing, moisture will build up in the walls from the inside and not be able to evaporate to the exterior.

The traditional method of damp proofing stone walls was to coat them with a lime-water wash produced by slaking quicklime in rain-water. The lime-water absorbs carbon dioxide from the air and deposits calcium carbonate within the pores of the stone and mortar, hence reducing the porosity to liquid but still allowing water vapour to escape. Such a treatment would be unsatisfactory where the stonework is to be exposed as decoration. Here more modern methods using silicones in special solvents are required and the help of an expert in masonry preservation should be sought.

It is easy to be misled into thinking that an old stone property is damp simply because it has been unoccupied for some time. Such apparent dampness normally disappears when the house is lived in, fires lit and good ventilation encouraged to hasten the drying process. Damp problems only occur where moisture is allowed to build up and lie permanently in the masonry, not where the stonework is continuously changing from a dry to a damp state.

Moisture-Associated Problems in Stonework

The ultimate result of dampness in stonework is the erosion of the stone, which in turn can lead to serious structural instability (Plate 29). Such a drastic situation is rare, although a certain amount of disfigurement, particularly in ashlar work, is quite common (Plate 30). The damage tends basically to be the culmination of both chemical and mechanical action and will be more marked in softer stone, such as sedimentary sandstone and limestone, than in igneous or metamorphic rocks such as granite and slate. Unfortunately soft stone is easier to work than the older harder forms, so it has been used more extensively for decorative building work, which therefore suffers greater erosion. Not only is the actual stone attacked but also the mortar which binds the stone together. So damage can occur even where buildings are erected out of extremely durable stone.

Chemical erosion is the result of acids forming in damp walls which dissolve the actual stone particles in the case of limestones, or the matrix binding these particles together in the case of softer sandstones. Acids are formed either from atmospheric carbon dioxide or industrial pollutants (such as sulphur dioxide) reacting with water in the walls. In urban and industrial areas these have caused considerable damage to old stone buildings. Even in rural areas chemical erosion occurs as a result of acids produced indirectly by algae, lichens and mosses which flourish on damp stonework and, once established, *keep* the stone damp.

Mechanical damage to damp stonework in temperate climates is invariably the result of frost action. One of the stranger properties of

(Above) Plate 29 Wall collapse as a result of erosion. *(Below)* Plate 30 Frost damage on ashlar as a consequence of rising damp

water is that it begins to expand, instead of contract, when cooled below 4°C. Such expansion of water within the tiny pores of stone and mortar causes the matrix to shatter, so that over the years exposed stone faces gradually flake away.

Erosion occurs where the structure is dampest. In old buildings this is generally a zone a couple of feet high right around the building just above ground level where rising damp ensures that the stonework in this area never completely dries out. Other localised areas of damage might appear where water lodges as a result of poor design, bad pointing, faulty guttering, or damaged downpipes and flashings.

Erosion of stone through dampness is a slow process and might at first sight seem to be too small a problem to be bothered with. However, damp walls transmit damp to other less durable materials where decay is far more rapid, with possibly disastrous consequences. The root cause of such damage must be tackled before attempting to cure the symptoms. For example, damp proofing floors and walls is essential before replacing stained plaster and rotting skirting boards.

Restoration of Masonry

Very badly damaged stone must be removed and replaced with new matching stone. This must be done a few stones at a time to avoid the weakening or collapse of the whole structure. Normally such severe problems are not encountered, and restoration is more of a cosmetic exercise. Algal and lichen growth should be treated chemically, rather than regularly and rigorously scraped away. Such growths generally flourish on softer porous stonework. Vigorous scratching over the years will erode the stone more drastically than anything nature alone can do. In fact in the stately homes and gardens of Britain meticulous and tidy-minded gardeners have caused more damage to beautiful stonework in a few decades than natural agencies have done in centuries.

Scraping not only damages stone, it is also ineffective since it cannot remove all the vegetative growth and can even spread it to previously clean areas. The rule is to spray it, not scrape it. The basic spray is a tar-oil wash, similar to that used to treat fruit trees in the autumn, which is almost 100 per cent effective when applied yearly in the spring.

A major problem likely to confront the new owner of an old stone building will be cleaning up the stone facework to draw attention to the stonework itself. This may involve the removal of old cement render or skins of lime which have been applied over the years, or simply repointing. Cement and rough cast renders are fairly easily removed by simply hacking off with a hammer, and cleaning up the odd stubborn area with the bolster or chisel. Lime presents more of a problem. Much of it is removed by chipping out the old mortar between the stones and then washing down the walls with a strong jet of water from a hose. However some lime invariably remains staining the centres of the individual stone faces.

Complete cleaning of stonework can be done by sand blasting (*see* Plate 10). This is suitable for most types of stone, including ashlar work, and is the most common cleaning method used on stone buildings in urban areas. In this technique abrasive sand particles are blasted with compressed air against the facework to cut a minute layer off the surface of the stone. The sand particles can be graded to accommodate different hardnesses in the stonework being cleaned. Sand blasting requires special equipment and skills and is not a DIY project. It must be undertaken by a firm specialising in such renovation work.

Lime responds well to acid treatment, which can be done without special equipment. Industrial acid is most commonly used on floors which have become stained with mortar during building and grouting work. This reacts with the lime in the cement, releasing carbon dioxide and breaking down the mortar chemically. The acid should be applied according to the manufacturer's instructions, brushed in with a stiff broom and then well hosed off with liberal amounts of water.

When working on walls, the wall should be re-pointed before the acid is applied to prevent the lime mortar in the walls being attacked. Small areas at a time should be tackled, working from the eaves down. Washing off must be very thorough to ensure that all the surplus acid is diluted and washed away, otherwise the stone itself will be attacked in time. Soft limestones and very porous stone should be treated with non-acid cleaning fluids. Special cleaning fluids are also required for polished and decorative stonework, so seek expert advice from the manufacturers to deal with these.

Re-pointing

Old neglected stonework generally benefits from the face-lift that re-pointing can provide, and often it can also cure many direct penetration damp problems. Pointing styles and techniques have already been discussed in Chapter 7, so all that needs to be added is some advice on cleaning the old mortar from the joints. The old mortar must be cut away deeply using a lump hammer and narrow cold chisel. Then a good depth of new cement mortar can be bedded into the joints. Before re-pointing the joints should be hosed or brushed free of dust and loose particles. The mix must be fairly stiff and incorporate a plasticiser.

It is best to work from the roof down so that any slovens and snubs of mortar can be cleaned off as you progress. Having chosen a pointing style, stick to it throughout the work, do not mix styles. If working to an existing style, either try to match it or, if you do not like it, re-point the whole building. Cleaning out the old joints is a slow and tiring job, and minor accidents often occur towards the end of the day. Always wear goggles to protect the eyes from flying chips of stone and try to alternate the hacking out with some other less tedious job.

Timber Renovation and Protection

Timber is far less durable than stone and provides a habitat and food source for numerous organisms which alter both its appearance and structural properties. A fairly high moisture content is necessary in the wood before it becomes susceptible to attack, even with the so-called 'dry' rots. It is therefore essential to keep timber in buildings from becoming permanently damp. Because freshly felled timber contains a very high moisture content, such 'green', or even partly-seasoned timber must never be used in building construction. The most durable timbers are well-seasoned hardwoods such as oak and chestnut which were traditionally used for the major supporting members of buildings. Nowadays softwoods are generally used instead; but although these are more susceptible to damage, better damp control in buildings compensates for this.

Dampness in timbers may arise in several ways. The absence of roofing felt and decaying slates or tiles may allow direct penetration of rainfall onto roofing timbers. Moisture from damp walls may penetrate into the ends of joists, rafters, and purlins causing them to rot where they are bedded into stonework. Rising damp in walls and floors may affect window sills, skirting boards and ground floor timbers, but more important, it may maintain a high level of moisture in the base of the main timber frame supports in a frame-construction building, leading to their instability and ultimate collapse. This inherent weakness largely accounts for the scarcity of old frame construction buildings, in comparison with those erected on mass construction principles where damaged timbers are easier to replace.

Another, often overlooked, means of increasing moisture content in timber is through condensation. This becomes a real danger in modernised properties where insulation, double glazing, draught proofing and higher living temperatures reduce ventilation and encourage the condensation of water vapour in colder roof spaces. Good damp protection is essential before replacing any damaged timbers. Otherwise, using modern softwoods, the problems will only occur again within a very few years. But take care that you do not *create* a damp problem by making your property too snug.

Fungal Attack

There are two main forms of fungal attack in timber generally classed as *wet rots* and *dry rots*, wet rots being the more common. These are generally due to infection by a species of *Coniophora*, the cellar fungus. The moisture content of the wood must be fairly high (approximately 35 per cent to 45 per cent) for an infection to occur. The fungus is completely killed by drying out the timber to 20 per cent or less moisture content, so this problem is most easily tackled by curing the damp and improving ventilation. Wet rots can also be cured by the use of fungicides, so any softwood used to replace old timbers should be pretreated in this manner as a normal precaution. The fungus lives off the cellulose in the wood, dissolving it away and leaving the darker lignin behind, so that they are sometimes called *brown rots*. In time the wood cracks up into small cubes and the timber loses all its strength.

The dry rot fungus *Merulius lacrymans* is an altogether more serious pathogen than *Coniophora*. Infection can occur at relatively low moisture levels and the fungus spreads rapidly through the timber reducing the interior of the wood to almost pure lignin while the surface cracks into dry, easily powdered cubes. Curing dry rot is difficult. All affected timber, plaster and plasterboard must be removed, together with a fair proportion of sound timber around the infected area. This timber should be burned immediately, not stacked. Otherwise the fungus will continue growing and spread elsewhere. All the remaining timber must then be treated with an appropriate fungicide to prevent re-infection from fungal spores present in the atmosphere. Causes of dampness must be eliminated to prevent spore germination. Where dry rot is suspected it may be worth seeking the advice of a firm specialising in such work. If they undertake to treat the problem, they normally offer a long term guarantee against re-infestation (Plate 31).

Insect Attack

A number of insects attack timber, well known examples being the death watch beetle in ancient buildings and the wharf borer in river and dockside regions. By far the most common and important pest is the common furniture beetle, *Anobium punctatum*, otherwise known as 'woodworm'. The larvae of *Anobium* feed on wood, preferably sapwood, and are the main culprits responsible for damaging timberwork of any form from the smallest stick of furniture to the heftiest roof beam.

The adult female lays her eggs inside the wood, generally in cracks or joints and on the end grain, anywhere where entry is made easy and the eggs can be well protected. On hatching the larvae bore into the wood, opening up channels and galleries. A heavy infestation can eventually reduce the interior of the timber to a fine powder. After metamorphosis into the adult stage the young beetles emerge from the wood leaving flight holes 1 to 2mm in diameter which are quite obvious to the naked eye (Plate 32). Where emergence is recent a small pile of bore dust can be found.

The presence of flight holes in the wood does not necessarily mean that the wood is still infected, for these are made only at emergence. However, the presence of dust *is* evidence of recent activity and an indication that infestation may still be present in surrounding areas (Plate 33). Even where no flight holes can be seen, there may still be beetle activity. Any signs of infestation within a roof must make all the roof timbers suspect. The presence of flight holes does not necessarily indicate that the whole timber is unsound. In old beams, particularly, the

Plate 31 On site treatment of timbers in an old box frame cottage *Rentokil Ltd*

(Below) Plate 32 Flight holes in timber following an infection with woodworm *Rentokil Ltd*. *(Bottom)* Plate 33 Internal damage to timber caused by woodworm *Rentokil Ltd*

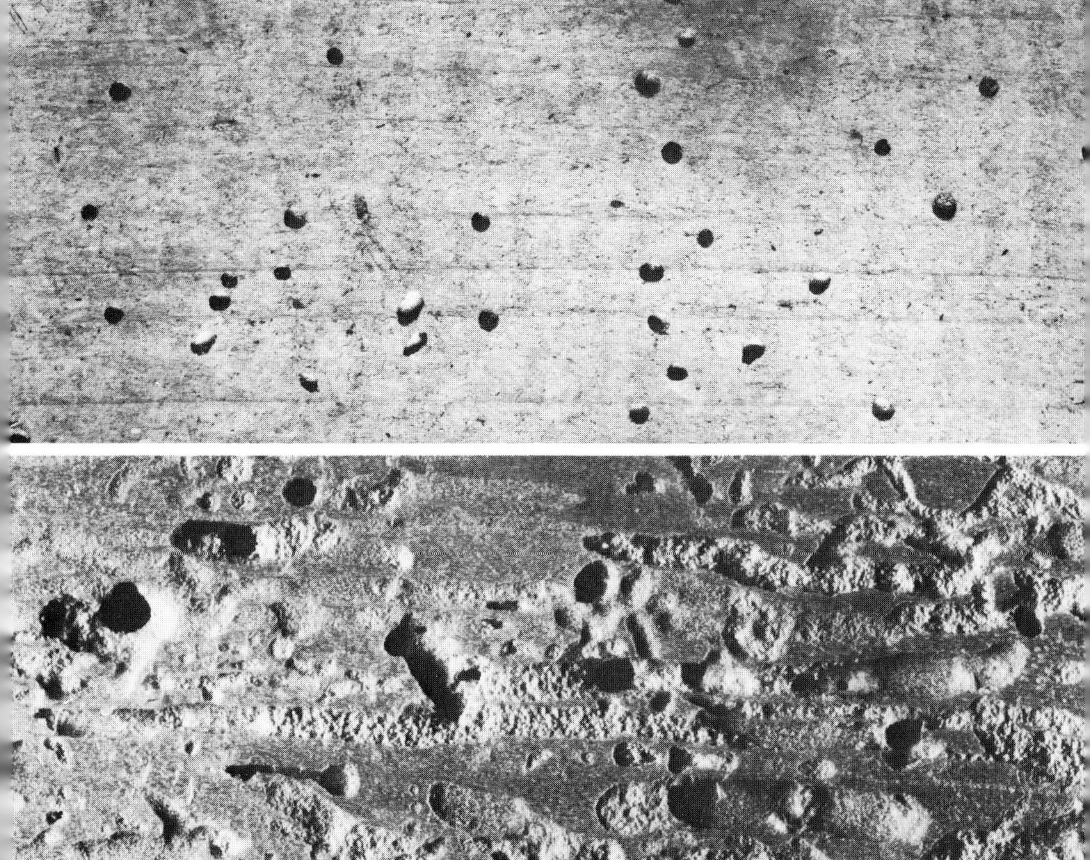

infection is likely to be restricted to the surface layer of sapwood, the bulk of the timber being made of heartwood which is unaffected.

Anobium does not attack living timber, but is unlikely ever to be eradicated since a plentiful supply of recently dead timber occurs naturally. The beetle finds most timber, from broken branches to dead ivy, quite satisfactory for her egg-laying activities. Fortunately where infestation is suspected chemical treatment is simple and effective.

Anobium damage must be given special consideration where a barn or outbuilding which has housed animals is being converted. For reasons that are not well understood the presence of animals causes changes in the timber which make it particularly palatable to the larvae. The structural timbers may well be very unsound and collapse under new loads during conversion.

Treatment of new timbers with timber preservative provides a very large measure of protection against woodworm attack. It is sensible to protect old timbers in the same way after any infection has been cured.

Working Old Timber

Heavy beams and joists in old rural buildings generally have a rough-hewn appearance, meticulously sawn and planed wood only being found in the grander homes. Most of such timber was hand-shaped with a special tool called an *adze* (Fig 73). These have largely disappeared from western cultures where most timber is bought as ready-cut softwood. It is, however, still an important tool in less advanced cultures where it is indispensable for many purposes, from shaping building timbers to fashioning dug-out canoes.

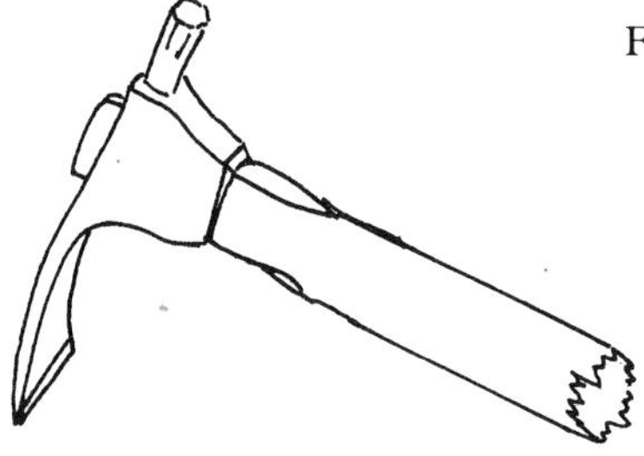

Fig 73 An adze for rough shaping timber

The adze is a two-handed tool which may at first sight be mistaken for a form of garden hoe or grubber. In fact I know a gardener who does all his hoeing with an old adze and will not be persuaded that he is ruining a rather rare and special woodworking tool! The blade or chisel of the adze is honed to a very fine edge and the delicate curvature of the chisel ensures that it cannot bite too deeply into the wood. By striking along the timber, with the grain, fillets of wood are cut away. The speed with which a beam can be trimmed and shaped with an adze, and the quality of the finish, are very dependent upon the skill and experience of the person using it.

The adze remains the ideal tool for producing a rough-hewn appearance and is excellent for renovating beams which have been superficially disfigured by wood boring beetles. For small timbers, and where an adze is not obtainable, a reasonable imitation 'rough-hewn-look' can be produced with a surform plane, although this takes considerably longer.

It is most important to remember that when replacing structural timbers the members which they support must either be completely removed as well, or otherwise fully and individually supported by some other means throughout the operation.

Newly worked wood is generally paler than old wood which has darkened with age and exposure to smoke and dirt. Antique dealers are the people to go to if you want to learn about methods of artificially ageing new unstained wood: all seem to have their favourite recipes. In general however, exposed structural timbers in old buildings were stained and this is still the simplest method of blending new wood with old. When buying stains be wary of the names given to the various shades. They can be very misleading, as the colour achieved depends upon the type of timber being treated. Always test the stain on a similar piece of timber and allow it to dry beforehand. Apply the lighter stains very evenly, otherwise darker areas will show where the wood receives a double application. Generally the matt finish produced by dark stains gives a better 'cottage effect' than clear lacquers or polyurethane varnishes. These are more reminiscent of Scandinavian style timber dwellings.

11
Alterations

Apart from the protective renovation of the original structure, owners of old stone buildings may wish to improve the comfort, utility or appearance of their house by altering what exists, rather than adding an extension. Tackling such alteration work provides invaluable preliminary experience before perhaps going on to add an extension later.

Windows

In old stone buildings the windows very often require attention. The frames may be rotten through lack of maintenance, the windows may not open because the frames have warped, and even if in good condition they may be so small that the rooms inside are dark and dingy. Historically windows were never as important as they are today. People were not concerned with views and would not have required light to read or write, because they could not anyway. They worked outside throughout the daylight hours and slept when darkness fell. Glass was very expensive and so was used sparingly, the windows only being required to provide sufficient light to allow the inhabitants to move around safely indoors and indicate the time to get up or go to bed.

Before replacing the windows some consideration should be given to factors apart from mere appearance. The new windows need not be sited in exactly the same place as the originals; indeed if you intend to alter the internal room structure their positions may well have to be changed. Old window openings can be built in with the materials removed for the new openings, so that obtaining matching materials is no problem.

The modern trend has been towards bigger and bigger windows. Large picture windows might afford the occupants a splendid view from the inside, but such vast areas of glass look totally out of character in a rural stone property when viewed from the outside. Even worse, such large openings can seriously weaken a mass construction building. A further disadvantage of excessively large windows is heat loss. The more glass you have, the more heat you lose. Even expensive double glazing will not entirely counteract such extra losses. Fortunately architects are beginning to adopt a more practical approach to house design and the trend is being reversed in favour of windows of a more sensible size. It is better to build a sun lounge as an extension which can be completely closed off from the main structure in cold weather than try to transform the house itself into something resembling a de-luxe fish tank (Fig 74).

Before attempting to remove the old windows it is essential that overhead joists are adequately and individually supported by stout timbers. The reason that the old window has become misshapen and will not open could be due to the decay of the lintel above so that the frame itself is taking part of the load. Removal of the frame could well be followed by the collapse of a large section of walling and the overhead floor.

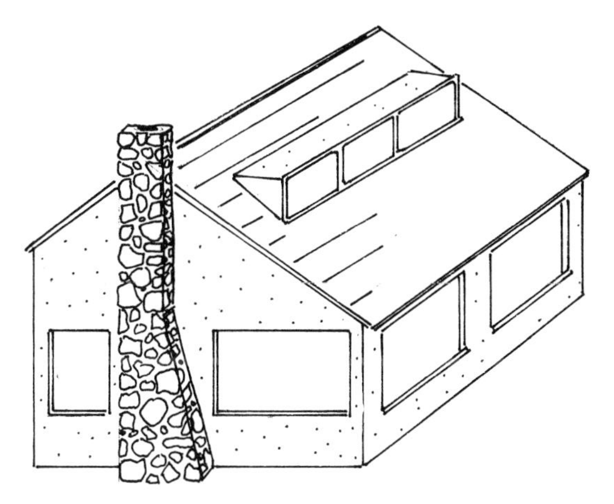

Fig 74 A de luxe 'fish-tank' conversion

Next remove the glass from the frames and store it safely; broken glass is dangerous, but the unbroken panes are re-usable, if not in the house then in the garden for cloches, frames and greenhouses. If the lintel is in fairly reasonable condition and still supporting the joists well, the old frame may be ripped out straight away. If not, then the frame is left and the stonework over the lintel removed in a naturally supporting arch-shape until the opening frees both the lintel and the frame. These can then be removed. The opening is progressively enlarged to accommodate the new frame. With stonework it is particularly important to ensure that this opening is considerably larger than the new frame width. If the frame only just fits the opening, then when the stone facework is rebuilt the window will be surrounded by small uniform pieces of stone completely out of character with the rest of the facework. Both large and small quoin stone needs to be used which must tie into the existing stonework.

Once the opening has been levelled off to the new sill level, building in the new frame follows much the same procedure as that already described for extension work (*see* Chapter 7, p. 115). However the walls will lack the cavity of modern buildings and it is a sensible precaution to set the frames well back to provide some measure of weather protection and to tack a strip of DPC material around the frame to prevent moisture moving from the stonework into the wood. When the new lintel is in place the gap above the window is closed off making every attempt to fill the wall as completely as possible, so supporting the existing walling above throughout the width of the wall. Only when the work has been completed and the mortar set should the timber supports be removed. The internal and external sills are fitted as described previously.

Doors

External doorways are not normally a priority for alteration unless they are particularly narrow or low. If the opening and frame is adequate but the door unsatisfactory a new door can be purpose-built to fit the opening. Should a new opening be required the procedure follows that described for windows in this and in Chapter 7 with one basic difference: the position of the bottom of the door is determined by the finished internal floor level and this should be borne in mind *before* altering doorways. Should the floors require renovation, calculate the new level of the floor and build in the frames to this. It may save a lot of excavation at a later date.

Stone Archways

Stone arches make not only a picturesque but also an extremely safe form of opening, whether as an alternative to a simple doorway through a gable end wall, or in a supporting wall to increase internal room size (Plate 34). To the inexperienced, the prospect of building an arch might appear daunting. However, once the principles are understood it is a relatively simple and very satisfying project to tackle.

Plate 34 Flattened arch of single pieces of sawn stone contrasting with the stone facework

Although arches offer great scope for variety in design, basically they can be divided into those that are curved and those that are made up of straight runs of stonework. Most arches require the initial construction of a wooden framework or 'form' to support the stone and to maintain symmetry during building.

Straight Arches

The term 'straight arch' is perhaps something of a misnomer since the very word 'arch' automatically conjures up visions of graceful curves. In fact the lintel seen over every doorway and window is an example of a straight arch, though straight arches are not just confined to the simple lintel form but may be seen where a peaked effect is desired.

The simplest way to build straight arches is by means of a double-lintel construction requiring slabs of massive even stone for the lintels, such as old pavings or sills. These arches must be supported on a framework of timber which is left in place until the mortar has hardened. This type of construction is illustrated in Figs 75–76. Two slabs of stone of matching proportions are placed in such a way that they lean together at the apex of the arch, while the remainder of the stonework is built over them. First, the supporting walling or pilasters are completed to a height that approximates to the required position of the base of the lintels. The wooden framework is then made up from stout straight timber such as 100mm x 50mm (4in x 2in) rafter to the exact internal dimensions of the whole arch and set firmly in position between the supporting stonework (Fig 75). Each lintel is set in position separately, the edges where they meet having been cut to form a mitred, narrow, vertical joint. At their bases the lintels must be locked behind a firmly set upright stone in the wall, or a pilaster (Fig 76).

These points are of great importance. Natural loads on the lintels force them downwards and outwards. If however, the point where they touch is bevelled, the edges of the stone are pressed tighter together the greater the load, thus transmitting the load outwards to the supporting work. If not 'locked' in this way, the downward force opens the joint, causing the arch to collapse at its apex (Fig 76). It is obviously important to accommodate these extra forces. Flimsy, hastily constructed pilasters will be pushed apart by the arch, as will any stonework that has not hardened before the lintels are set in position.

If the lintels cannot be cut at the apex to the required angles, the locking effect may be achieved by the use of a *keystone* between them. This will be trapezium shaped in section and will have the effect of tightening the joints under load (Fig 76). With the single horizontal type of lintel construction, the main forces are all downwards, particularly at the centre of the lintel. The peaked or curved arch, though more difficult to build, provides a far superior type of construction since it redistributes the loads to the supports.

Build the stonework over the lintels working from the supports to-

Fig 75 Wooden form in position for construction of a double lintel peaked arch

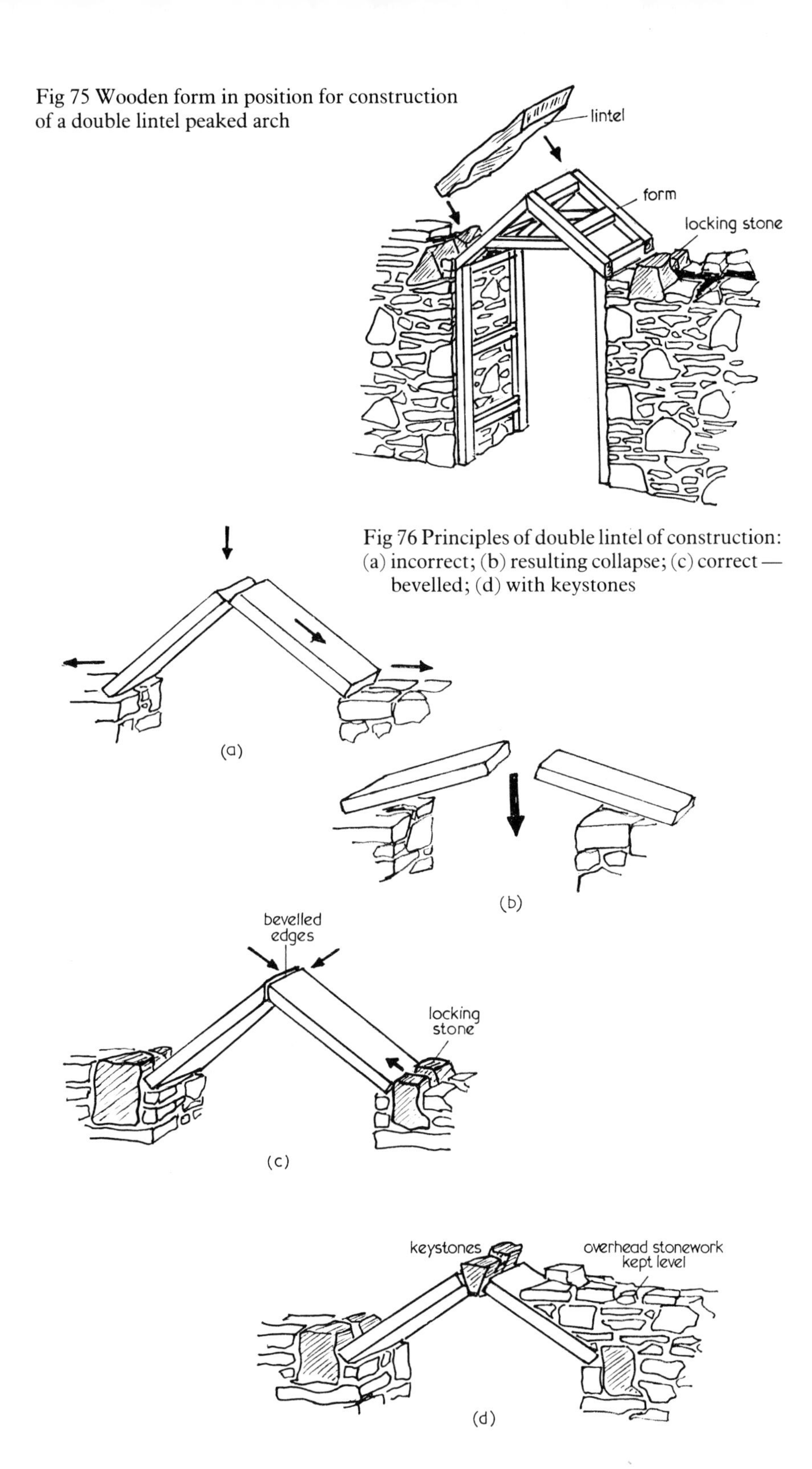

Fig 76 Principles of double lintel of construction: (a) incorrect; (b) resulting collapse; (c) correct — bevelled; (d) with keystones

wards the apex, tying the stonework well back into the supports. Do not slope the stone up the lintels but keep it horizontal as with normal building (Fig 76). This will provide greater strength as well as a more attractive finish. Copings and decorations are a matter of personal choice. Only when the arch is finished and set should you remove the timber frame and clean up mortar snubs with the hammer and cold chisel. If you are contemplating a series of such arches the timber framework can be used again and will ensure that all your arches are of identical proportions.

Peaked arches may also be built without using the double-lintel construction. Instead, the supporting arms are made up of selected shaped stones with keystones at the apex and where the arch joins the pilaster (Fig 77). The timber frame used here, though of the same shape, must have cross supports beneath the arch (see the next section on curved arches). This may be covered in hardboard or ply to provide a complete supporting area to work on. This makes the building easier but unfortunately prevents you from seeing the under-arch facework and from cleaning out the joints before the mortar has set really hard.

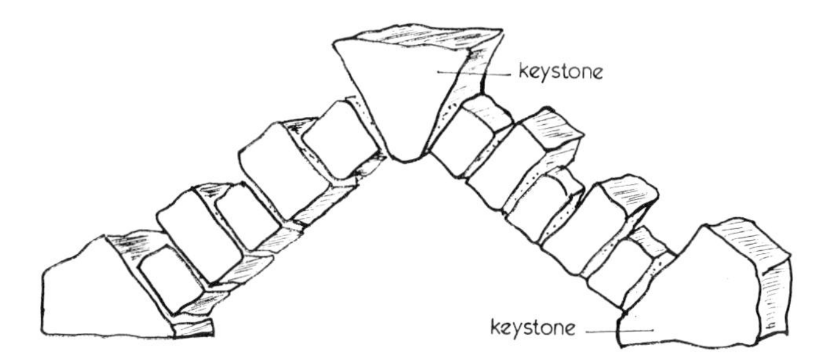

Fig 77 Shaped stones for a peaked arch constructed from separate units

The approximate shapes of the keystones are important and are required for each face of the arch. Their shape and orientation is outlined diagrammatically in Fig 77 and the stone between should be evenly matched and rectangular. Proceed with building as for the double-lintel construction and, with the frame in place, build over the arch evenly from each side, finally setting the centre keystone in place. Stonework above the arch itself should again be built on the horizontal plane and tied well back into the associated walling.

Curved Arches

The curved type of arch is not only the most beautiful to look at, it is also — if built correctly — the strongest form of arch construction and a most satisfying achievement for the stoneworker (Plates 35, 36). The choice of stone from a random pile of rocks, and their rough shaping to form the arch are perhaps the most important primary considerations. If you do not feel up to selecting your arch stones, visit a firm that

(Left) Plate 35 Archway showing how the individual stones have been cut to key and tie together. *(Right)* Plate 36 A fine decorative ashlar arch

specialises in sawing and dressing stone. Take with you an exact template of the proposed arch preferably in wood. They will then cut the stone to produce a perfect shape and fit, and you will be shown how to 'build by numbers'.

The more determined, those who relish a challenge, and those who believe that their arches should be built of the same random material as the rest of the work, must constantly be on the look-out for evenly matched trapezoidal blocks of the type used in the construction of a round pilaster, but they must be still larger. This time the facework is on the inside of the curve, and the stone should be trimmed with this in mind.

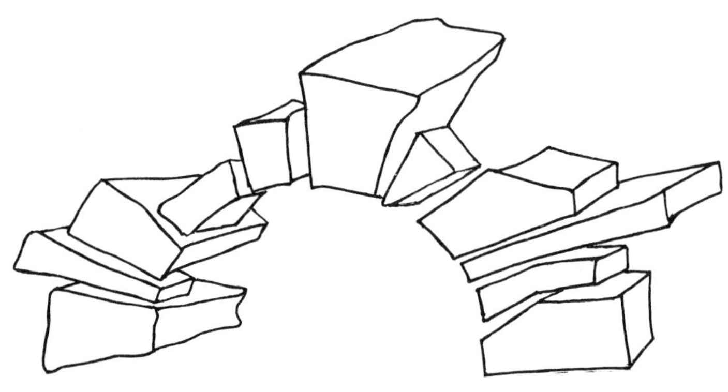

Fig 78 Some useful shapes of stones for curved arches

As with the straight peaked arch, three shaped keystones are very important and some useful random stone shapes for arch construction are illustrated in Fig 78. While building the arch, constantly remind yourself that the main thrust is downwards and outwards from the apex to the supports. Build to maximise this effect, so that the greater the load, the tighter the individual stones in the arch lock together. With perfectly shaped, cut stone no mortar should be required to keep the arch in place once the central keystone is in position. The shape of the stones and the forces they are subjected to will do this naturally.

For normal sized openings the best form of curve is a semicircle of the same diameter as the distance between the supporting walls (Plate 37). For larger openings the curve will be shallower. Whatever the curve shape it must be measured accurately and drawn out on a sheet of firm wood such as blockboard. Roughly saw out the shape, then rasp it down to produce a smoothed arc. This template is now used to cut out a second identical shape in the same wood.

When satisfied with the semicircles, cut lengths of true timber so that each of these, plus the thickness of the blockboard, measure the same as the thickness of the stonework. Use these to assemble the form as shown in Fig 79. A piece of hardboard may now be tacked round the curve and trimmed to size, producing a rigid and exact support and shape for the arch. This is then fixed in position between the stonework supports at

Plate 37 Semicircular arches over windows

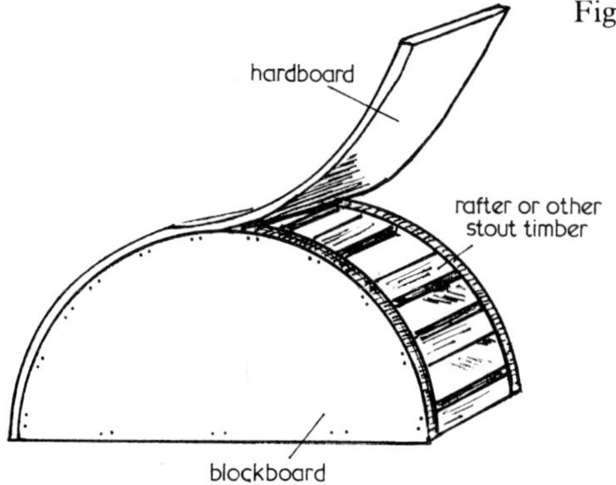

Fig 79 Simple form for a curved arch

the correct height by means of stout timbers, as shown for the double-lintel construction (*see* Fig 75).

The arch stones are built up over the frame from each side as with the peaked arches, and the frame can be marked to indicate the exact centre of the arch to aid positioning of the crowning keystone. Use the stone shapes as illustrated (Fig 78) and avoid great gaps that have to be filled with mortar. If your stone is perfect the two faces could well extend across the width of the arch, but this is most unlikely. To infill this gap,

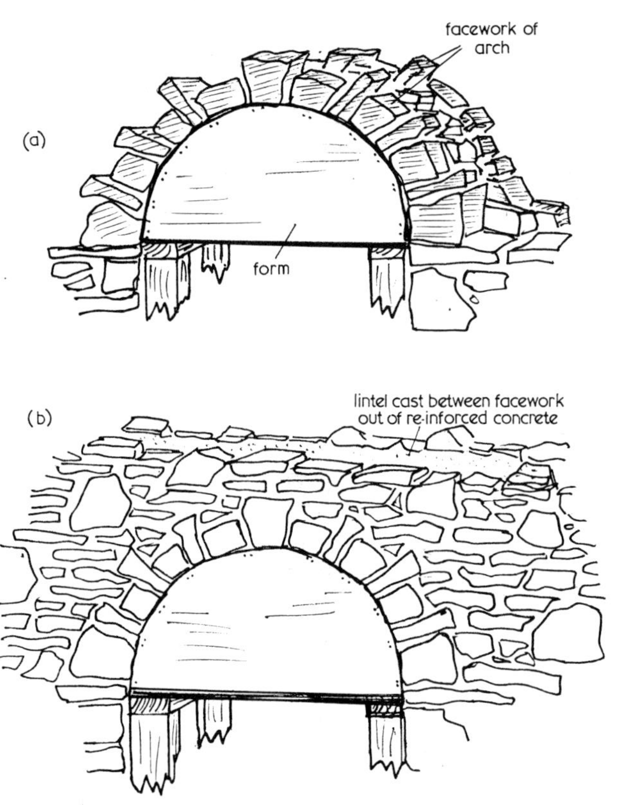

Fig 80 Casting a lintel over a curved arch: (a) stone in position; (b) formation of lintel

first allow the outside faces of the arch to harden, and clear away any loose mortar. Select stones that will lock down on to the back of the facing stone, mortar these into position (Fig 80), or infill with a concrete lintel as described below.

Build up the remaining facework over the arch as indicated above, leaving a channel between, except where the faces are tied across. When these are hardened, pour concrete into this channel and lay metal reinforcing rods into the concrete, so that they extend well over the supporting stonework on each side of the archway. When this sets you will have a reinforced concrete lintel bonded to, but invisible behind, the facework (Fig 80b).

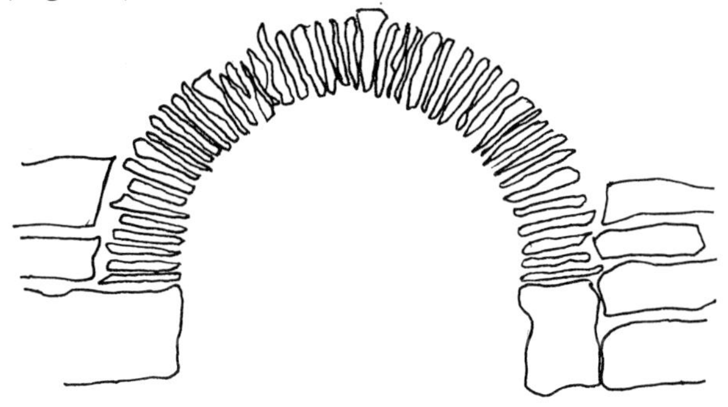

Fig 81 Curved arch produced from thin sheets of random stone

If shaped stone cannot be obtained, arches may be built on the same principle and by observing the same rules, with very thin sheets of stone (Fig 81) to produce a simple and pleasing effect.

When all is completed, remove the frame and clean up the stonework beneath the arch, even if it means cutting right back and lightly repointing the work. Goggles are essential.

Overhung Arches and Supports

Apart from this method of constructing arches using a timber form, arches and flared supports can be produced by a technique known as *corbelling* or *overhung building*. A *corbel* is a projection from a wall or some other structure and, by continuously overlapping a series of corbels, an arch effect can be produced. Corbelling is particularly effective where a pillar or panel needs to support an overhead structure that does not lie directly above the main support (Plate 38).

Corbelled stonework can only be achieved with a good supply of narrow long stone since most of the length of the stone must be bedded well back over the stone beneath. In other words, the weight of the bulk of the stone counteracts the portion of the stone that is unsupported. For this reason, wide corbelled spans are not recommended, because the stones above the centre of the span, which are subjected to the greatest load, will not be supported by the pillars on each side.

Plate 38 Part of an old fireplace with a corbelled pillar supporting two lintels

When building a corbelled stone arch, start with the shorter stones first, progressively increasing the length of the stones as the span grows; in this way part of the corbel will always remain over the main stonework support. Small spans are quickly constructed in this manner, which is ideal for producing decorative alcoves in otherwise fairly uniform stone walls, and can be most effective within buildings.

Internal Rooms

Old rural cottages generally have poky little rooms, but once an extension has been added there is scope to alter both the shape and size of the original rooms. Usually the whole of the original ground floor of a 'two-up-two-down' property is amalgamated into a single large living room, the kitchen and bathroom being incorporated into the extension. This type of alteration is shown in the plans in Chapter 3.

Before starting any such alteration the whole of that part of the building must be examined to ensure that the operation is structurally feasible. Where supporting walls are removed other forms of support are going to have to be provided. Solid upstairs partition walls may have to be removed and light timber and plasterboard partitions erected in new positions over structural beams beneath. In extreme cases the whole of the upper flooring may need to be removed and the joists replaced in a different way.

Obviously the manner in which such an alteration is undertaken will depend entirely upon the existing form of construction and therefore only general guide lines can be given. In the example shown in the plan details (*see* Figs 8, 9), a fairly extreme situation has been chosen where, because of the large spans, the whole of the first floor must be re-designed to give it adequate structural support. So be warned, what at first may seem to be a simple matter of knocking down a couple of walls and re-siting a staircase, could prove to be a major and most expensive undertaking. However, on the plus side, it should be remembered that with careful demolition, all the boards, joists and existing timbers can be re-used, so reducing expenditure on new materials.

The existing structure is detailed in plan form in Fig 82a and the proposed alterations in Fig 82b. The whole of the upper floor must be cleared before any ground floor work begins. In this case, this would have to be done at some stage anyway, since the upstairs rooms are to be altered too, but in general it is best to relieve the loads on the floors from the beginning. By going carefully and bearing in mind the structural problems involved at all times there should be no need to remove all the floor boarding and joists. But jacks and a plentiful supply of timber will be required for supports as the work progresses.

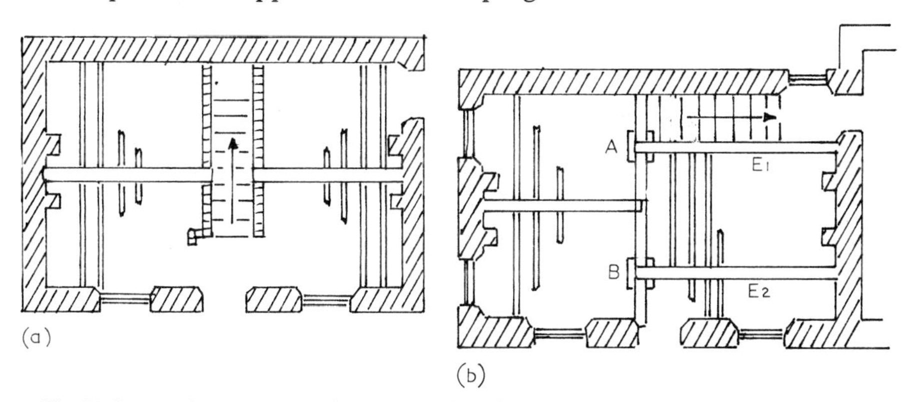

Fig 82 Converting two rooms into one — first floor joist and beam details: (a) original; (b) proposed alteration — A and B, vertical supports; E1 and E2, new beams supporting joists

The most important structural members will be the vertical posts marked A and B in Fig 82b, which must be erected *before* any further construction can proceed. These provide intermediate support for the main beams which in turn provide intermediate support for the joists. They must be accurately finished to the required height and rigidly bolted to the concrete floor. Since the supports will be exposed within the room some thought must be given to their siting and final appearance. They can be of girder iron which is later clad in stone to produce a circular or square pillar, they can be of painted tubular iron or of timber fitted into a metal shoe. In any case they can be disguised to some extent by plants, shelving, or seating around the base.

With the vertical supports in place a transverse beam can be erected to take over the supporting function of the west wall of the staircase (Fig 82). This beam extends right across the room and runs parallel to the joists. Although it supports the central beam in the west room it does not support the one in the east room which is still carried on the other staircase wall. While it is possible to repeat the same procedure for the east room, the finished effect with four structural uprights within the new room would be far from pleasing. Fortunately the problem can be approached in a different way.

At this stage the end of the main beam in the east room is supported by an acrowjack next to the staircase wall, the internal walls are demolished and the staircase removed. The floor boards, joists and finally the main beam is taken out so that the whole of the ceiling is removed. This may sound drastic and appear unnecessary but it is important since it saves the joists which would otherwise have to be cut and replaced. The only new timber required will be the main beams E1 and E2 in Figure 82b.

The main beams E1 and E2 are raised in the positions indicated and are supported by the original gable end wall and the vertical posts already in position. The new position of these beams has further advantages: they no longer enter the chimney breast creating a possible fire hazard, and E1 can double as a trimmer for the new stairwell. The joists are then re-laid, fixing those running between E1 and E2 first and only cutting for the shorter runs between the beams and walls at the end.

With the floor in position the timber framework and plasterboarding for the upstairs partition walls can be erected in the new positions.

Staircases

When dismantling a staircase it is most important to be certain that the walls confining the staircase are not supporting the floor members above. Staircases are generally moved to permit both downstairs room enlargement and to provide corridor access to first floor rooms and extensions. The most popular replacement is with an open staircase set against an eaves wall in the main living room (*see* Figs 9, 82).

Plate 39 Domestic stone spiral staircase *British Tourist Authority*

New staircases are usually purpose built by a joinery firm to suit individual requirements. They must also satisfy the building regulations for private stairways, which are quite complex. Anybody thinking of building a staircase themselves should first look at the regulations. Fitting the staircase is a fairly simple procedure requiring only basic joinery skills.

Before the staircase can be fitted, the stairwell has to be opened in the first floor. This means cutting away the floor boards and joists, fitting a trimmer joist and jointing the trimmed joists to the trimmer (*see* Figs 59, 82b), either by hangers or appropriate joist connections, for example a housed joint or complex tusk tenon joint. Further rigidity is provided by the vertical newel posts at the ends of the staircase which run from the floor to the connection of the trimmer with the untrimmed joists (*see* Fig 82b).

Apart from the simple straight open staircase, a wide variety of other forms are available. Metal spiral staircases are popular where space is limited downstairs, but beware since they cause problems on the first floor. The fitting of more complex types is best undertaken by the suppliers of the staircase themselves.

Historically wooden staircases are fairly recent innovations. Until the late eighteenth century access to the first floor level in small dwellings was generally by means of a ladder. A form of the stone spiral staircase common in castles and church towers was built into some stone houses, though these are rare and their presence is often concealed from view. Such a staircase was usually sited in the gable end wall alongside a fireplace. It would have steeply tapered steps and make half a complete turn between the ground and first floors (Plate 39). With the introduction of the more practical wooden staircase these stone spirals were generally bricked in and forgotten, only to be rediscovered during alteration and extension work.

Such a late discovery, however, may not be the bonus it would seem at first. Acquaintances of mine bought a cottage and began to build an extension similar to that illustrated in the plans in Chapter 3. It was only when they started to break through the very thick wall beside the fireplace to provide ground floor communication with the new extension that the stone spiral was discovered. Rather than lose this unusual architectural feature they re-sited the opening to the extension on the other side of the fireplace, altered the room layout in the new extension at considerable expense, and renovated the stone staircase.

With large rooms it is possible to build internal straight staircases from stone, but these are very bulky constructions and can be overpowering even in a big room. Also they look rather odd built against a plastered, papered or painted wall. They should definitely only be built where they can blend back into similar stone facework behind. In view of the regulations governing new stairs and the complexity of construction, it would be best to seek professional advice and practical assistance from an expert if attempting such a task.

Fireplaces

Open log fires in large, bold, stone fireplaces fascinate and delight everybody. In fact during my years in business, more of my contracts concerned the renovation of old fireplaces or the construction of new ones in stone than anything else. After carrying out several renovations I formulated four maxims for approaching fireplace work:

1 Things are very rarely what they appear to be at first.

2 No two fireplaces are exactly alike and one must strive to emphasise the individual character.
3 Remove as little stonework as possible and avoid breaking through the chimney breast into the flue.
4 Be bold with the building so that the fireplace rather than the television becomes the focal point of the room.

Following these rules often meant that, although the open hearth and flue remained in its original form, the rest of the renovation work was concerned with making new additions. These attempted to alter the style to suit an enlarged room while retaining the character of the original fireplace. What is *totally* out of character is to put in a factory-built fireplace, often advertised as 'stone', but merely made of stone cladding bonded onto a backing, which bears no relationship to the rest of the stonework in the cottage.

If suitable stone is not available *old* brick can be an effective substitute, particularly where the internal stonework has been rendered over and none is left exposed. Brick was traditionally used for flues and fireplaces for its superior heat resistant properties compared with many forms of stone. The very pleasing brick fireplace shown in Plate 40 was built in a small terraced stone cottage by the owner with no previous building or architectural experience.

Plate 40 Fireplace constructed of old bricks in a small terraced stone cottage

In an old stone building original fireplaces are likely to be found in the gable ends (*see* Fig 8), though one or both may be blocked off. Originally the two fireplaces would have performed separate functions, one providing an open hearth to heat a parlour or living room, the other providing heat for cooking either on a range or on an open hearth with side ovens in a kitchen area. With the introduction of electricity and the common addition of a lean-to kitchen/washroom extension early this century, the redundant kitchen fireplace was usually closed off. If the rooms have been converted into one large living room the normal approach is to renovate one of the fireplaces and close off the other.

Before deciding which fireplace to renovate, it is worth asking why one room should have only *one* fireplace. Originally the fireplaces heated only small rooms. Now a much larger area needs to be heated. A single open fire creates a very localised area of heat, leaving the rest of the room quite cold. Although I have yet to persuade anyone to renovate and use both fireplaces, I remain convinced that it has unique advantages. Families naturally wish to do separate things yet remain in contact with each other. A large room allows this, but more important, a large room with two focal heat points allows it comfortably. The television can be viewed in comfort at one end of the room, whilst at the other a book can be enjoyed, homework studied, models constructed and so on, still within the family framework and within the comfort zone of an open fire.

Of course extra trouble is involved in keeping two fires going when one might do, and fuel costs have to be considered: so in general a choice is made between the two. In purely financial terms, if one fireplace is already blocked off and the other still functional and only in need of improvement it would seem sensible at first sight to stick to this arrangement and improve the existing fireplace by cosmetic renovation. However, this may be a false economy in the long term if the functional fireplace is on an exposed gable end and the closed hearth in the centre of the building by virtue of a new extension (*see* Figs 8, 9). In terms of thermal efficiency it is then far more sensible to renovate the closed fireplace and so heat the house from both sides of a central flue, rather than losing much of the heat to the countryside at the exposed gable end.

There is one further way in which the internal gable wall can be heated and the original flue and chimney system used without having an open fire there. Where a new kitchen extension is added beyond the gable wall as in the plans in Chapter 3, a solid fuel cooker can be installed which utilises the original flue and chimney stack from the reverse side. Personally I would give much consideration to putting in a solid fuel cooker, since these have become extremely efficient in the last few years. Unlike the huge cumbersome stoves of the past, modern solid fuel cookers are compact, easy to regulate and can be remarkably catholic in their taste for fuel, coping equally well with modern smokeless fuels, ordinary coal or even wood. Furthermore they not only provide cooking facilities but heat domestic water supplies and support a limited central heating system if required. During the heavy snowfalls of the winter of 1978/9 our own solid fuel cooker supplied the needs of several families in a North Yorkshire village isolated for three days by drifting snow and damaged power lines.

Having decided which fireplace to renovate, re-design or improve, the practical considerations of such a project must now be discussed.

Functional Fireplaces

As I have said, renovating an already fully functional stone fireplace may be looked upon as more of a cosmetic than a structural alteration. If the fire surround and chimney breast have been rendered over and plastered then this should be hacked off to expose the stonework from floor level to ceiling. If the room is fairly narrow it is even more effective to clear the stonework over the whole wall area at that end of the room (Plate 41). The stonework can then be examined, damaged stone and odd brick replaced and the whole structure re-pointed.

Plate 41 A renovated stone fireplace with a wooden lintel

If the hearth lintel is in poor condition this must be replaced. Like window lintels, a wide choice of materials is available, although it must be borne in mind that these will have to be able to withstand prolonged and intense heat. Before removing the old lintel it is essential that you examine and understand the construction of the chimney breast and flue, which means examining it both inside and out. In the fireplace renovations I have carried out two types of construction were predominant, though variations occur within the two basic forms.

In one form the hearth opening is often massive, the chimney breasts and flue totally constructed of stone and the flue rises pretty well directly above the hearth even though it rapidly narrows to the chimney stack. The stonework to the inside of the flue is rough and unfinished. This type of fireplace is the more primitive of the two forms and fires lit in the hearth often burn unpredictably and belch smoke into the room during blustery weather (Fig. 83a).

In the other basic form the hearth openings tend generally to be smaller and the chimney breast and flue is lined with brick, stone only being used on the exterior. The brickwork is generally corbelled out on the inside of the chimney breast so that the flue is set back on the hearth opening rather than rising directly above it (Fig 83b). Fires lit in these hearths tend to burn better and blow back less smoke in windy weather.

In the all-stone type of construction the hearth lintel generally carries all the stonework. In the brick and stone type the lintel may carry both the brick and stonework or the stonework only, the brickwork being supported by metal strapping behind the lintel (Fig 83b). With the latter form it is important *not* to disturb the brickwork during demolition and replacement of the lintel since this will ensure that the fire will continue to work well and no seepage of smoke will occur through the chimney breast as a result of disturbance.

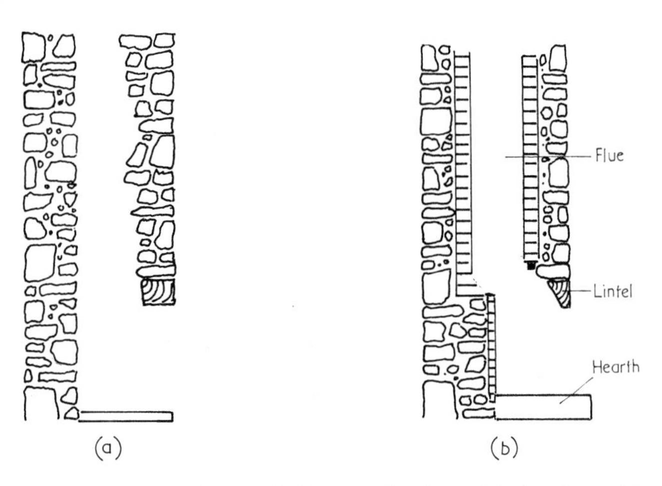

Fig 83 Sections of two basic forms of old stone fireplace: (a) simple straight flue; (b) brick lined throated flue

Whatever the construction, the stonework must be removed from above the lintel in a self-supporting arch, working from the middle of the lintel to each end, until the lintel is clear and can be safely removed. During demolition, if the chimney breast is brick lined, it is sensible to provide additional support for this by means of timbers from the hearth to prevent accidental damage from falling stone.

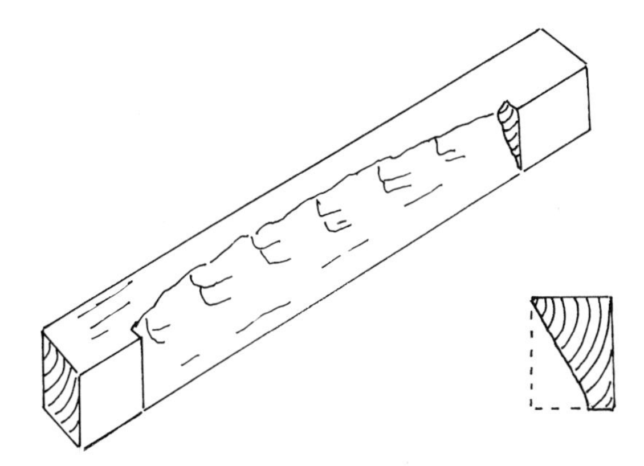

Fig 84 Detail of shape of wooden chimney breast lintel

Traditionally wooden timbers or a solid piece of stone were used for the fireplace lintel, and it is important to ensure that these are not too deep. A deep lintel provides a broad base upon which stonework is easily built up above, but is detrimental to the efficient operation of the fire, causing a dead space above the fire which allows smoke to curl back into the room. Ideally the lintel should be tapered away to almost nothing at the bottom, broadening out towards the top, and the stonework/brickwork should continue to constrict the flue in a gradual manner so that the fireplace becomes *throated* with the chimney flue lying behind the hearth (Figs 83, 84). It is rarely practical to achieve this ideal, but the nearer you approach it, the better. If installing a wooden lintel it should be shaped as shown in cross section in Fig 84. This greatly reduces the fire risk which is always a problem with wooden lintels. You can often tell a genuine old wooden lintel by the way it has become charred into this natural shape over the years.

Before rebuilding the stone facing to a brick-lined flue, it is worth rendering the exposed brickwork on the outside to seal any cracks which may have occurred in the joints during demolition, purely as a precaution. When the render has hardened the stone facework to the chimney breast can be rebuilt and the whole structure re-pointed.

Where the chimney is not lined with brick, the re-building at first attempt may not prove totally satisfactory and considerable seepage of smoke could occur through the stonework. This is not due to amateurish workmanship so do not be disheartened. It is extremely difficult to build in between the lintel and existing stonework and produce a perfectly sealed joint. Moreover, the mortar tends to shrink on drying, leaving tiny gaps through which smoke can seep. Be prepared to light a fire and make it produce as much smoke as possible to identify the main seepage joints. These can then be cut out and redone more solidly. Infuriatingly, stopping these often leads to seepage from other more minor cracks! I prefer to temporarily seal all the leaks progressively with soggy newspaper until smoke seepage is stopped altogether and then repair all the faulty joints marked by the paper. If the seepage is very bad and cannot be cured in this way a chimney liner may have to be installed and in this case further advice should be sought to cope with your particular problem.

The hearth itself may also require attention and I must confess that I prefer the raised type of hearth I first noticed in mid-Wales in my youth. I find that a hearth raised 25 to 30cm (about 1ft) above floor level not only provides a more comforting warmth when in an armchair beside it, but is exactly the right height for toasting your toes in cold, damp weather!

In many old fireplaces the distance between the hearth and the lintel is excessively large, resulting in a poor draught through the fire and curl back of smoke into the room. Raising the hearth is an easier and more pleasing way of overcoming this problem than lowering the lintel or installing a fire hood. The best height can be judged by experimenting with lighting fires on an old concrete slab supported on bricks and blocks at different levels, and the permanent stone hearth finally built into place when the most satisfactory position has been found.

Although the fire itself may be burned directly on the hearth stone both this and the fireback will inevitably crack and splinter in the intense heat. It is far better to buy or have made a free-standing grate, but make sure that this is large enough to take decent sized logs and is in keeping with the fireplace itself.

Large stone fireplaces and logs go naturally together, yet they consume a vast quantity of wood which always seems a problem to store conveniently to hand unless you have prepared for it during the building. No one wants to keep going out into the cold and dark for an armful of wood, so continue the fireplace along the wall using the alcove between the chimney breast and wall corner to make an intermediate store for sufficient kindling and fuel to last several days. Symmetry, if desired, can be achieved by creating a ledge on the other side for radio, stereo, television or whatever you wish.

Sealed Fireplaces

The renovation of a sealed fireplace is more difficult to discuss since the specific problems will not become apparent until the fireplace has been opened up. Approach the matter optimistically with the consoling thought that if a fire once burned there it can do so again. As mentioned earlier the fireplace that is sealed off is most likely to be the one that previously housed a kitchen range for cooking. But in very old buildings the range was often a later addition to an even older open fireplace.

All covering plaster should be stripped away from the chimney breast and the newly exposed surface examined for horizontal and vertical joints which indicate where an original opening was reduced to fit the range. This is often made easy to identify by the fact that an old stone chimney may have been altered using bricks which stand out against the stone. All the new additions must be removed to expose the original structure. Before any further renovation is done the chimney must be swept clean and a fire lit in the opening to discover the particular characteristics and behaviour of the fireplace. Do not forget to go into the upstairs rooms to see if the flue has been cracked and smoke is escaping there; or to ensure that the chimney flue is clear before lighting the fire!

Once the characteristics of your particular fire have been discovered, renovation work can proceed to improve both appearance and performance in much the same way as described for functioning fireplaces. In extreme cases the flue may have to be re-lined or the chimney breast taken down completely and rebuilt with an internal brick throating. In others simply altering the hearth height in relation to the lintel may be all that is required to produce a satisfactory fire.

Wiring and Electrical Points

It is sad that very often good renovation work is marred by poor attention to the finishing detail, and perhaps electricians are amongst the greatest culprits here. It is certainly sound practice to rewire an old stone property, but thoughtless to allow wires to trail over a feature stone wall and switches or plug points to be attached to rough chunks of wood protruding out of the stonework.

When wiring into stonework, a continuous channel should be cut deeply in the mortar joints, the wire laid into this and the groove pointed over to hide it. Switches and points should be set flush into the stonework by removing a stone and building the appliance into the facework with smaller stones. Overhead wiring should run along the back of the joist which is closest to a wall so that it is not visible from the room itself.

A little attention to such details make a considerable difference to the final appearance of the job. The same applies to plumbing: pipes which must be exposed should follow the contours of the walls by being fixed in horizontal and vertical sections, rather than criss-crossing the walls in direct diagonal paths. It is worth paying a bit more for copper pipes that can be polished up so that they look as though they are *intended* to be exposed as an attractive feature of the room.

In such instances if you are employing subcontractors it is essential to insist from the start that the work is carried out to your requirements.

12
Conversions

Space within a rural stone property is often restricted, but this may be compensated for if a number of outbuildings are included. Such buildings may be in various states of repair and hapazardly arranged, but nevertheless can very often be converted into useful additional rooms to relieve some of the pressure on space within the house itself. One section of this final chapter discusses the conversion of outbuildings into functional but 'non-domiciliary structures'. The remainder of the chapter deals very briefly with the more major type of conversion of a large stone building such as a barn, into a home.

Conversion of Outbuildings

The first question normally asked about the conversion of outbuildings is: 'will I need planning permission?' Generally the answer is no, provided that the building is not extended or altered in external appearance. Further information concerning planning requirements is given in Chapter 3: but if in doubt the local planning authorities should be consulted. Similarly such conversions need not be passed by the building inspector unless they form an integral part of the main dwelling. However the building regulations should still be followed because they provide a ready guide to safe building practice.

Before conversion, the outbuilding should be considered as basically four sound walls supporting a good roof. If either the walls or roof require repair then these jobs should be done before any conversion work is begun. Special attention should always be given to the roof timbers which must be thoroughly checked for damp and insect or fungal damage (*see* Chapter 10). Remember to pay particular attention to those parts of the timbers which are in contact with or buried within the masonry. These are the most likely parts to be affected. Also check for signs of nesting birds. House martins, swifts and swallows can not only prove a nuisance but prolonged nesting in the same sites ultimately causes the decay of both the timber and masonry around them.

Whether the expense of proofing the building against rising damp is justified will depend upon its eventual function and the type of internal finish being applied. It is usually unnecessary unless you intend to live in the rooms, or the damp is very bad. Penetrating damp can be controlled less expensively as described previously: just the provision of adequate ventilation is often sufficient to solve that problem.

Design Considerations

One essential feature often overlooked is that outbuildings are usually converted to cater for activities which would interfere with the smooth operation of domestic routine if carried out in the house. They are often converted to provide workshop, games room or garage facilities. So the design can be tailored to suit the future function of the building, with out the usual constraints that apply to house alterations..

Plan the interior to meet your requirements before erecting partitions or installing or enlarging windows. For example (Fig 85) if converting a large deep outbuilding into a garage, make sufficient space for two cars side by side, not one in front of the other — even if you only have one. (Otherwise the car you require always seems to be stuck at the back!) If making a two storey conversion do not automatically wrestle with the problem of siting an internal staircase. This not only takes up valuable internal space on both floors but restricts design freedom. Consider first the use of external steps, keeping the two floors isolated, if the rooms are not going to be used at night.

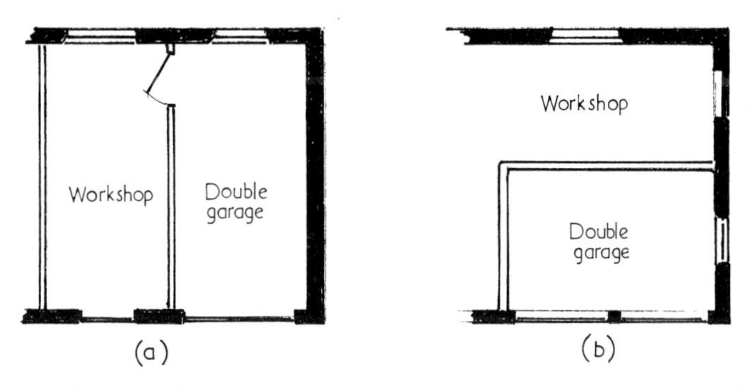

Fig 85 Converting part of a large barn to accommodate a workshop and garage: (a) poor design; (b) improved design

Children's Rooms

For those with a young family a playroom away from the house is a real bonus, and may be well worth the sacrifice of a spacious workshop. The children will probably spend more time in their playroom than father would in his workshop, especially as he will no longer need this excuse to get away from them. Be safety conscious in the choice of siting and design. In two storey structures put the playroom on the ground floor to prevent such accidents as falling out of windows or down the stairs: your children will have friends to play who may not be as well disciplined as your own. Furthermore they will create far more noise dashing about the timber floor overhead than on the solid floor beneath.

When building a playroom try to consider two main points:

1 Decide what function you want it to perform, eg wet day play area, quiet room for homework, storage space for outdoor toys, etc.

2 Think about what the children themselves will get out of it. If its prime purpose is to allow the children freedom to let off steam, particularly on wet days, make sure that they are going to be *happier* to do so out there than under your feet in the home. In other words build to their needs and requirements and not to impress other parents.

If you have young children you will initially have to make all the design decisions for them. But as they get older they will tell you what they want and even design it themselves, so the comments that follow really apply to children in the age group of about three to ten years. Such children are small, and while this can be used to advantage in the home to keep things out of reach it should not hamper them in their own room. So from the start try to view the design from your knees.

Set light switches and door handles considerably lower than normal and use handles of the lever type rather than knobs which must be turned. Internal doors only require a ball catch so that they can be simply pushed open and swing both ways. Window panes will almost certainly get broken at some time, so choose frames with small panes which can be inexpensively replaced. Huge picture windows just ask for trouble! Try to avoid installing plug points where young children will be left to play unattended. If you choose to provide plug points so that the whole place can be wired in one go for future use in a different function, box the points in so that the children cannot play with them.

Heating will be the main problem. when it is warm enough not to require heat the children will probably be outside, they will only want to be inside when it is wet or cold. Electric or gas heaters are both dangerous and expensive to run, and an open fire is out of the question. If it is not practical to provide radiators, a good solution is the closed form of woodburning stove. Though somewhat expensive to install these are very cheap to run, require little supervision and maintain an adequate background heat. In addition those wet macs and wellingtons can be dried around it rather than clutter up the house. Such stoves should be fully guarded of course.

Do not go in for expensive wall and floor coverings. They are not likely to be appreciated and, in any case, most toys run far better on linoleum, concrete or plain board floors. A degree of comfort can be provided by a couple of secondhand rugs, or a piece of left over carpet and some large bright cushions in one area, while the remainder of the floor is left bare. Children love to decorate walls with stickers, posters, drawings and so on, so make it easy for them. Fix sheets of fibreboard to the walls from the floor up to the height of a single panel for pinning pictures to. These can be interspersed with a couple of sheets of blockboard painted matt black to provide blackboards. A ridged wooden ledge under the blackboards is useful for keeping chalks and dusters handy. The remainder of the walls can be left bare or whitewashed over to receive posters and works of art. Furnishings should be spartan, only adults relax quietly in armchairs! A stout old table with the legs sawn down may be all that is needed, children preferring to kneel on a cushion to draw rather than sit, legs swinging, on an uncomfortable adult chair.

Garage Conversions

If converting a barn or part of an outbuilding into a garage, decide from the outset if it is simply to be a place to keep the car, or whether you will want to work on the vehicle. As I have said, make it large enough to accommodate two cars side by side. In a rural area a second car for taking the children to school and doing the shopping could turn out to be essential.

Large, up-and-over metal garage doors are quite out of place on the front of a converted stone barn. In certain areas the planning authorities have quite positive views about what is or is not acceptable. Wherever possible try to match it with the traditional door style of your area. Note the method of door and frame construction, as well as the style, and then copy it yourself or have it made to your specifications.

The large span required for the lintel will probably mean that steel girders will have to be used. Fortunately these can be clad with stone on the outside to blend fairly well with the existing stonework. When demolishing large areas of stonework for such openings, take great care to ensure that the rest of the structure is supported. If making such an opening into the eaves wall of a cruck-framed barn, check where the cruck beams run and site any opening between them.

If the garage building joins onto the house, or a children's playroom, the regulations concerning fire protection must be observed and the building will have to be inspected. These additions could prove to be expensive, so consult the authorities when considering a garage conversion as an integral part of the house.

If the garage is going to be used for repair work it is a simple matter to cater for this during the conversion stage. Dig out a working and inspection pit before you concrete in the floor, put in an overhead girder for lifting heavy weights and supply plenty of sockets around the room for inspection lamps and power tools. You may not be an enthusiast yourself, but your son could turn out to be one. In any case there are many minor jobs which it would enable you to do for yourself which cost a lot if taken to be done by the professionals. It is also an added amenity which might well help to sell the house if necessary in the future.

Tool Sheds and Fuel Stores

If the outbuilding is a large one it is not necessarily the best policy to divide it up by numerous partition walls into a lot of separate units. Not only does this involve considerable expense in materials, remember every wall requires an opening, but it also makes the building less versatile. If the barn has been used for livestock in the past one area may be divided into stalls already. Use these divisions, improving rather than demolishing them. Who knows, your daughter could become pony-mad and you would have to put them back.

Stalls make excellent compartments for fuel. Your solid fuel supplies, particularly logs, will take up a great deal of space, especially if you are going to saw enough to keep that big open fire roaring through the winter. You will also need kindling. Rather than be tied to splitting odd bits of planking or logs every day of the winter, collect old wind-fallen twigs from the woods on dry days throughout the year and store them. They break easily into convenient lengths and have a fire going in no time if stored in the dry. Similarly, tools can be hung and work-benches and shelving sited conveniently, without the need for separate tool stores and workshop. If a partition is required, a simple bay constructed of a single skin of blockwork will be perfectly adequate.

Derelict Small Buildings

Where a small building is in an advanced state of decay it may well be worth considering a conversion which does not require the total restoration of the building to its original form. Such a conversion is illustrated in Plate 42 where a small stone building had collapsed at one gable end

Plate 42 Conversion of a small outbuilding into a combined toolshed and greenhouse

Plate 43 Two storey barn conversion

bringing down part of the eaves wall and roof, yet leaving the other gable end sound. Using the original materials a small toolshed was built and re-roofed inside the sound gable end. The remaining eaves walls were lowered and levelled off and a wooden greenhouse frame erected on them. Planning permission in this instance was obtained by consultation rather than submission of detailed plans, and the design was regarded as quite acceptable. The only new materials required were the timber framework and glass for the greenhouse and the window frames and doors for the shed; the whole structure cost less than a ready made greenhouse of a similar size, and was far more attractive.

Large Barn Conversions

If considering the conversion of a large barn into a multifunctional unit, the project should be approached in the same professional manner as the renovation or extension of a house. Proper plans should be drawn up, by an architect if necessary, planning permission obtained and a work schedule organised. The work can be carried out as described for the extension in Part II, that is by yourself using subcontractors, or can be passed over entirely to a builder. The one distinct advantage of such conversions is that the major work involved in erecting the shell and putting on the roof is already done. Caution is needed when partitioning first floor storeys to ensure that the floor construction is adequate to cope with the additional weight it will have to carry.

No attempt is being made in this concluding section to describe *how* various types of buildings can be converted into homes. The description

Plate 44 Two storey barn conversion

of each type of conversion could fill a book in itself. Instead I briefly outline and illustrate what types of stone buildings can and have been turned into homes.

Barns are undoubtedly the most common type of stone structures converted into homes. They fall into either the single or two storey category. Long, low barns, found mainly in Scotland, have the drawback of a vast floor area compared to their bulk. This tends to isolate some parts of the home from others, perhaps an advantage at times with young children! Heat loss from such properties is disproportionately large, so that any such conversion should have insulation high on the list of priorities.

Two storey barn conversions produce a more normal type of house, though often a very large one (Plates 43, 44). Their outlines also remain 'barn-like' which deters those who prefer their homes to be less obtrusive. Bank barns of the type occasionally seen in the Lake District are rare and generally suffer from recurrent damp problems and poor light.

Other types of structure may be converted, such as old windmills, watermills, lock houses, toll houses and so on, all relics of a previous age and all with their own particular charms and drawbacks. They may also carry with them requirements to maintain the property in a certain way if it is a listed building. Although grants are available for such buildings, these tend to be more token than substantial. Generally the conversion and renovation of these properties involves very considerable expense on the part of the owner.

Appendix

Table 1A Costing — Materials

Item		*Price (ex. VAT) in relation to 1 cwt cement*
		£
Cement/cwt		1.00
Builders' sand/tonne		3.70
All-in sand and aggregate/tonne		6.30
Bricks:	common/1000	33.70
	facing/1000	37 – 56
Block:	ordinary thermal/m² (10 blocks)	1.37
	Thermalite/m²	1.75
	concrete external/m²	1.54
Roof tiles:	clay pantiles/1000	110 – 185
	clay plain tiles/1000	93.00
	plain concrete tiles/1000	130 – 170
	1st quality slate seconds/100	7.40 – 18.50
Slaters'	roofing felt/15m roll	4.45
	insulated felt/6m roll	3.90
PVC	Guttering, 100mm ½ round/6m length	3.42
	Downpipes 60mm/6m length	3.45
	Bends/each	0.52
	Angles/each	0.53
	Soil/Vent piping 100mm/4m length	5.00
	Soil/Vent pipe bends/each	1.60
	Underground drainage piping 100mm/6m length	5.60
Clay	Drainage piping 4″/2′ length	0.63
	Pedestrian manhole covers/each	5.25
Fibreglass septic tank complete with kit		148.20
Glass:	3mm/sq ft	0.30
	4mm for larger panes/sq ft	0.35
DPC	100mm/12m roll	1.04
	300mm/12m roll	3.12
DPM/approx. 13m roll		7.78
Lead flashing 300mm/6m roll		11.49
Timber:	100mm matchboard/m	0.16
	100mm skirting/m	0.20
	75 x 50mm rafters/m	0.19
	180 x 75mm purlins/m	0.76
	100 x 50mm wall plate/m	0.26
	125mm PTG floorboarding/m	0.24
	180 x 25 mm ridge board/m	0.40
	150mm fascia board/m	0.32
	windowcillboard/m	0.98

Table 1B Costing — Some Projects

Item — excluding labour	*Approx. price in relation to 1 cwt cement*
	£
Concrete foundations/m³	20.10
Concreting subfloors/m²	2.20
Cement screeding floors/m²	1.06
Internal blockwork/m²	1.90
Timber floor boarding including joists/m²	5.44
Timber work for pitched roofing using collared double purlin construction/m²	5.87
PVC guttering complete (excluding weatherboarding)/m	1.20
Glazing in 3mm glass/m²	3.70
PVC underground drainage/m run	1.60
Clay underground drainage/m run	1.80
Average manholes (with screw down covers)/each	44.00
Felting and battening/m²	0.60
Roofing with secondhand slates/m²	2.30
Roofing with pantiles/m²	3.80

To obtain actual costs multiply figure in price column by present cost of a 1 cwt bag of cement. For example: if cement costs £2.75 per bag then common bricks would be approx. 33.70 x 2.75 = £92.00/1000 and concrete for the foundations would cost approx. £20.10 x 2.75 = £55/m³.

Table 2: Various Types of Mixes for Different Construction Projects in Stone

Type of mix	*Type of work*	*Sand–cement ratio*	*Consistency*★	*Additives*
Concretes	Infilling	8 – 10:1	2 – 3	
	Foundations	6 – 8:1	4 – 5	
	Bases	6 – 8:1	4 – 5	all-in aggregate
	Lintels	4 – 6:1	4	
Mortars	General walling	5 – 7:1	1 – 2	plasticiser
	Topping-off	4 – 5:1	2 – 3	plasticiser and bonder
	Blockwork/ brickwork	4:1	2 – 3	plasticiser and bonder
	Pointing (internal)	3 – 4:1	1 – 2	plasticiser
	Pointing (external)	3 – 4:1	1 – 2	waterproofer
	Paving (thick)	6 – 8:1	2 – 3	
	Paving (thin)	4 – 6:1	3 – 4	
	Grouting	2 – 3:1	0	
	Cladding	3:1	3	bonder
	Flooring (tiles)	4 – 6:1	3 – 4	bonder

★Wetness scale from 0 – 5, equivalent to no water (0) up to a very wet mix (5).

Table 3: Amounts of Materials Required to Make Concrete

Volume concrete (cu metres)	*Amount of cement (no of bags)*	*Amount of all-in aggregate (tonnes)*
0.25	1	0.63
0.50	2½	1.20
0.75	3½	1.80
1.00	5	2.40
2.00	9½	4.80
3.00	14½	7.20
4.00	19	9.60
5.00	24	12.00
10.00	47½	24.00

Bibliography

Barry, R. *The Construction of Buildings*, Vol 5, Supply and Discharge Services, Granada, 1978
Bayliss, R. *Carpentry and Joinery*, Hutchinson, 1963
Brunskill, R. W. *Illustrated Handbook of Vernacular Architecture*, Faber, 1978
Burdett, G. *David & Charles Manual of Home Electrics*, David & Charles, 1981
Grundy, J. T. *Construction Technology* Vol 1, Edward Arnold, 1977
Grundy, J. T. *Construction Technology* Vol 2, Edward Arnold, 1979
Hall, E. *David & Charles Manual of Home Plumbing*, David & Charles, 1982
Handisyde, C. C. *Everyday Details*, Architectural Press Ltd, 1976
Harrison, J. A. C. *The DIY Guide to Natural Stonework*, David & Charles, 1979
King, H. and Nield, D. *Building Techniques* Vol 1, Chapman and Hall, 1976
Martin, S. *Build Your Own House*, Stanley Paul, 1978
Richardson, S. A. *Protecting Buildings*, David & Charles, 1977
Woodeforde, J. *The Truth about Cottages*, Routledge and Kegan Paul, 1979

Note
The Craft Council, 12 Waterloo Place, London SW1, have compiled a register of local craftsmen able to undertake specialist work in connection with restoring old buildings — thatchers, masons, etc. A leaflet is available but the Craft Council recommend that the conservation officer at your local county planning department be contacted as a first step.

Acknowledgements

I should like to acknowledge the contribution of the following people and organisations for their assistance and helpfulness in the preparation of this book:

Mr G. M. Davies of the Planning Department of Harrogate Council for help with the section on planning and for supplying the photograph reproduced in Plate 1.

All the various persons in the Department of the Environment at Harrogate who assisted me with the section on local authority grants for home improvement etc.

The Manager of the Leeds Permanent Building Society at Ripon, N. Yorks, for help with the section on mortgages.

Mr John Crosby of Messrs Bolton & Crosby, Architects, who drew up the plans specifically for this book besides providing other helpful advice.

Rentokil Laboratories Ltd for supplying the photographs (at very short notice) reproduced in Plates 16, 28, 31, 32 and 33.

The British Tourist Authority for providing and giving permission to preproduce the photograph used in Plate 39.

Messrs Ripon Builders Supplies Ltd and Messrs Ferguson-Foster Ltd, both of Ripon, North Yorkshire, for their courteous and willing help in supplying the information for Appendix 1.

Mr Jack Cooper, particularly, for providing the photographs reproduced in Plates 15, 38, 41 and 42 and for all his work in developing and printing the photographs taken by my wife and myself.

Above all my wife, Jacky, for not only typing the manuscript but improving its readability and suggesting ideas, handling the correspondence, obtaining most of the photographic material and producing a splendid daughter at the same time.

Index